THE TRAIN STATION

SCRIPTA HUMANISTICA®

Directed by
Bruno M. Damiani
The Catholic University of America
Advisory Board

THE TRAIN STATION

VINCENZO BOLLETTINO

Scripta Humanistica® 172

Publisher and Distributor

Scripta Humanistica®

1383 Kersey Lane
Potomac, Maryland 20854 USA
Tel. (301) 294-7949
Fax. (301) 424-9584
Internet: www.scriptahumanistica.com
E-mail: info@scriptahumanistica.com

S.H. #172

I.S.B.N. 1-882528-63-8

Price: $59.95

PRINTED IN THE UNITED STATES OF AMERICA
2014

To my wife, Linda, and to our treasured children,
Vincenzo Natashi
Maria Alessandra
Vjolca Thalia
Antonella Francesca

The Train Station

Chapter One

The door to the house was locked with the heavy metal key. Night had given way to a windy morning amidst thunder and sheets of rain that, once or twice during the year, would come down the mountains looking to nestle behind every stone wall in the clustered caves of Sheshi.

The shadows that followed, uniting and separating, touched every stone as if to take with them their invisible luster, so familiar in years past. That morning, the stones on Sheshi's narrow street had felt especially soft and shiny, like so many falling stars on the night of Saint Lawrence.

We climbed as one, the four of us, holding fast to the brightness of the stones and to the sound of the bells whispering from the clock in the center of Sheshi. The cold, wet streaks of the wind forced us to flock together much as the few street lights fading away in the deep emptiness of the precipices where barren foothills were cradled in thick layers of gray clouds. When we reached the top of the hill, we could see other clouds, white and cold, descending from the mountains to lay a transparent sheet of ice on the rooftops.

The train station stood on the tallest knoll overlooking all of Sheshi. The massive stone and brick structure had been built by men in black shirts who had worked in unison, moving to the sound of a whistle which hung about the collar of another black shirt. Now the platform of the train station stood deserted. Along it, prickly shrubs were immobile, unperturbed by the wind; their stiffness added to the firmness of the platform's steel and white stone.

Sitting in the waiting room reserved for third-class

passengers, my mother's fingers, always so firm and flexible, seemed bent by the silence and the feeling of impotence that reigned in the place. It was close to five o'clock when the tiny silver bell on the front wall of the train station began to announce the imminent arrival of the train. The sun was just beginning to peek from behind the lowest of the seven mountains when I saw the approaching locomotive puffing its way out of the tunnel. I watched my mother grow pale and her fingers grow as stiff as the cold on top of the treetops. Her mind wandered to a time which only she could remember. It was the bleeding hour of her first birth. The coarse white sheets her mother had given her had been in the family for generations. They were completely drenched in blood. The large copper pot of boiling water was emptied to clean the creature one step away from the mother, both pride and loss wrapped together. The round-faced boy with wide open eyes left an indelible mark on all those present in the house.

The grandmother took her firstborn grandchild to the village's central fountain; there she dipped him three times into waters that all deemed to be unquestionably sacred. The women busy scrubbing barely raised their eyes to get a glimpse of the sparkle in the old woman's eyes. That night the house shook from a minor earthquake. The cracks in the walls grew deeper and wider. Days after, the grandfather traced the cause of the tremor to the brightness of the eyes of the newborn. An invisible line connected his eyes to the cracks on the walls.

I look at my mother's face now. I hear the first sound of the bell at the train station. I can clearly see my great-grandmother's presence in her wrinkled forehead.

In the village they called my great-grandmother "Faela." Sitting next to the ashen walls of the wood-burning fireplace, she would wait impatiently for the first signs of spring. She stood tall and erect and had gone completely gray. She claimed fifteen births for herself, although only eleven children survived. One of the nine founders of the village, she was one of the great mothers of Sheshi. It was rumored that she had been the one to name it.

At the yearly gatherings, Faela was carried to the village square on her oak chair; it took a dozen men to lift the seat of mystery. No one could trace when or by whom the chair had been made, or how its oak pieces were held together. The men hastened to lift it when the town fiddler played the call of the serpent. The ceremony began at the first sound of the bell from the white chapel, which had been brought stone by stone from Constantinople by those mountain men with sharp golden moustaches and eagle eyes. The church had been reconstructed upon the place of the sacred cave where night met the day and the earth, the depths of the sea. There, the elders whispered, sound became color and fire fused with water. At the center, an altar of silvery waters gave birth to fish with paws and wings. The mother serpent breathed life into the flowers. The bells rang louder and louder, suffocating all sounds, both human and animal. The earth trembled, fusing rock upon rock, leaf atop leaf, sound with sound. The great oak chair moved toward the tabernacle; eyes were bathed by the rays from her face, a burning red mask. Alone, with wings spread, the great mother descended into the deep waters. Then throngs of screaming women wet their lips and sharp nipples with the sacred waters, and the burning rays turned pink, the carmine streaked with white. Distant greens and grays clothed the slender bodies, collecting the ashes scattered in the pool of water. The women begged for strength as the throbbing structure fed itself from heartbeat to heartbeat.

The full moon had painted the sky with elongated lines of smoke rising from the stone chimneys of the homes. It was the time of the evening meal. The partition of bread by the one at the head of the table traveled silently from one end of the town to the other. That bread had been baked by the rays of the sun chasing butterflies on a sea of yellow fields and eager sailing boats in search of blue horizons. The houses floated into the arms of the night. Darkness moved firmly to cover the rooftops. The windows shot, promises broken, flesh with flesh. The serpent sucked the last drop of milk from her breast, slowly winding its way down to the nest under the pile of wood left there since last spring, the smell of its olive bark changing from year to year.

The serpent had made its way to the waiting room of the train station. The train master, clothed in the state uniform, turned on the lights of the station's platform. The dusty railroad carriage opened its door to receive the passengers barely discernible through the black vapor. With a sharp pull, the conductor sealed the entrance to the coach and ordered the train engineer to move on.

The mountain mist quickly engulfed the last of the light of the train station. The smell of the earth, recently plowed for early spring planting, seeped through the cracks of the carriage as it made its way through the mountain tunnels. The heavy rains had turned into a soft drizzle, rendering the landscape fuzzy. I looked at Great-Grandmother Faela's house at the end of the village as the train emerged from the last tunnel of the seven mountains. Sheshi seemed like a lonely drifting cloud in the emptiness of dawn. Then I recalled Great-Grandmother Faela's last words to my mother. "Just remember, every home has four walls no matter where it stands."

My mother, who had been staring at me as I tried to cling

to the fading speck of whiteness of Sheshi in the distance, suddenly said, "Make certain you never forget the road back to the village." For the remainder of the morning, she spoke no more. Those who left the village tormented by the dreams of a better place full of riches would never again be able to recover their lost memories or to recognize themselves in the mirror of time.

The very name of Sheshi was rarely mentioned, even by the village's elderly. Many a time I had heard stories of wanderers who, through unexplained circumstances, found themselves beset with fears on the road that led to the village. No one in Sheshi could ever precisely locate the source of their fear. It was said in secret that it lay deep in the first water well dug deep under the floor of the Church of the Dead. Not even the oldest of the elders who boasted of having gone beyond one hundred years by three decades knew of its beginnings. "It must have happened before things assumed their present shape, before light separated itself from darkness, and before the eyes of the people were covered by the gray mist that comes down from the seven mountains," he explained when asked.

The train had come out of the last tunnel as I fixed my eyes on the man seated in front of us in the compartment; he offered a piece of bread to his companion with a slight movement of the arm. The slice came from a round loaf of bread baked days ago. The woman quickly glanced around the compartment and then decidedly pushed his hand away from her. The two rarely exchanged a look nor spoke a word to one another for the remainder of the trip. Their faces, expressionless, locked behind an impenetrable wall of mistrust, were seductively immutable. The woman, grave, looked no different than the long array of elders in Sheshi sitting outside their homes waiting for a letter or for the sudden appearance of their loved one on the dirt road that led to the train station.

Distance had blanked out the few remaining houses at the extremities of Sheshi. The seven mountains were a mere winding, broken line on the distant horizon. The train had ventured outside the sacred space. The sermons at the tabernacle at the center of Sheshi had vanished into the depths of silence.

I recalled the bells of the Church of the Dead. At one time they rang faster than the flight of the black swallows around the bell tower. The almond trees that lined the round space of the village square were no obstacle to the passionate call of the bells. From the dilapidated door on the side of the altar emerged the town's priest, Prefti Vlasë. Barely in his fifties, he prized his two books...a copy of a lost Pelasguian text transcribed into Latin by an Albanian Imam on top of the minaret and a list of songs in ancient hieroglyphics.

With unshaven face and deep black circles under his eyes, Prefti Vlasë made no attempt to hide the sadness of the times. The Mass he had prepared to celebrate had no beginning and no end. Amidst yawns and closed eyelids, he said, "I see nothing but disrespect for the old, abandoned by their young ones. Greed and immoral behavior have extended their tentacles into every corner of Sheshi. The holy water in the font has been shedding bloody tears. I see fewer and fewer of our people opening the door to the church."

To the people who took part in the daily service, this lament was just part of the same song. Prefti Vlasë could not keep his eyes from looking towards the side window of the church, where he could catch a glimpse of the sky that reached his native village, Mali e Sezë (Black Mountain), at the foot of a crooked, barren mountain that changed color according to the position of the sun. The town had been carved out of the black mountain six hundred years earlier by a group of Albanian mountaineers who called themselves "gheghiërs." Among these people with watery blue eyes and sun-colored moustaches, no woman was to be found.

During the celebration of Mass, Prefti Vlasë never failed to hear the heavy breathing of the long caravan of Albanians as they moved towards the "Promised Land." He lifted his eyes and saw his flock as bereft as he was behind the altar of the presence of his Master. He knew exactly where the ceremony began and where it ended in the Holy Book in front of him. He saw the round, multi-colored window on the front of the church darkened by the gray clouds hanging over it.

It had been the great-grandfather of Prefti Vlasë who had decided to send a messenger to the fallen city of Constantinople to relay a request: he wished for Taras, the leader of the city now called Istanbul, to release to them the captured Christian women in recognition of the service of the Albanians to the Turkish pashas. It took fifty years for the women to reach the village of the Black Mountain.

The women arrived in long wooden carts pulled by fifty enormous white bulls with horns twisted in the shape of a quarter- moon. One by one, the giant bulls were systematically slaughtered during the festivities that lasted for more than thirty days. The merchants who had brought the women to the village all died of water poisoning on the first day of spring. The death of the merchants, with their egg-shaped black hats, did not come as a surprise to the elders of the village. However, the well from which the merchants had satisfied their unquenchable thirst for hours was forever closed to the public. For many years, the children playing near the well would relate to their mothers the suffocating cries which came from below the spring and which, at times, surfaced to the top like green water bubbles, each with a slice of the rainbow.

The black swallows, which had not been seen for so many months that the village folk despaired of ever again following their flight through the corridors of the sky to reach their wheat fields, suddenly flocked to the square from miles and miles around the countryside. The birds pecked frantically against the floating droplets to free the anguished callers, but to no avail.

Years later, those who could still recall the miracle of that late afternoon in March never tired of recounting the event to the young ones; they endeavored to make as few modifications as possible in order to preserve the intensity and the anguish of the captives' cries. No one had any difficulty at all in believing these events; nor did anyone question the personal additions with which, despite their best intentions, the elders enhanced the sequence of the happenings.

In time the women of the village came to compare the pregnant water droplets to the hours of birth that yearly lacerated their bodies and opened deep cracks in every house that lined the main square. The wounds carved in the cement were left exposed to the blustery winds of November and the heavy snows of January. For generations, no one in the village dared to get close to the fissures to assess the yearly damage.

The odor that continually emanated from the lacerations rested on leaves of the almond tree. Only the unfailing rains of the first weeks of fall lessened the feeling that the earth was rotting in its womb. Prefti Vlasë was fated to carry that odor to his tomb. It was how the people of Sheshi identified his resting place even after they had forgotten what he looked like. For this reason, the cemetery caretaker saw no need to reprint the priest's name with lead or to indicate the dates of his stay on earth after the marble tomb took a direct hit from a bolt of lightening that twirled down from the sky that hovered over the tallest of the seven mountains. Everyone in Sheshi seemed convinced that the fumes which accompanied Prefti Vlasë in the last days of his life would outlast everyone else in the village and travel even beyond their boundaries. For the young men of Sheshi who had gone to the four corners of the earth, that odor was an unmistakable verification of their place of origin.

Prefti Vlasë's benediction to his flock was followed by the sound of the bell announcing the end of the novena. In the faces of the few parishioners who attended the service the anxiety to return home was apparent. Night descended quickly on Sheshi. With the church empty, Prefti Vlasë hurried to close the doors to avoid the chill evening air. He had quite a way to go before he could reach the protection of his home.

The village's narrow streets had become abruptly engulfed in a voluminous silence. The priest followed the distant silhouette of one of his worshipers. Wrapped in her dark shawl, she hurried steadily towards her home. The nimble- footed old woman was known throughout the village as Sina. "What would it take to show these people the way to salvation?" Prefti Vlasë queried. "What steps could I take to free them from their perennial fears of the inevitable destructions that lurk in the darkest depths of the night?" A feeling of impotence prevented him from even attempting to find an answer to the burden he had painfully carried with him ever since his arrival in Sheshi.

The empty house on the edge of the village glistened with a lonely yellow light. The volcanic stone structure, shaped like a cone, could be seen from every corner of the village. The people of Sheshi knew too well what Prefti Vlasë undertook every night as he walked from the Church of the Dead to his home. He had to cross every street before reaching it. Behind their doors, some listened attentively to the struggle between Prefti Vlasë and the cries of fate. "Is he wounded?" some asked from the safety of their homes. Others, terrified of the undefined wailings, filled their doors with crosses and garlic wreaths to ward off the evil voices from trying to sneak through their locks or through the invisible cracks in the walls. Those nights were long and dreary, and no one dared open the door in the morning until Prefti Vlasë announced his victory over the devils with three piercing tolls from the church bells of the great Church of the Virgin of Constantinople. This ritual was repeated at sunset and at the crack of dawn. No one knew when it all had come to an end.

Mother must also have been thinking of Prefti Vlasë. She had gone through her prayer beads three times since we had left the train station. The train easily traveled along the straight tracks with a continuous monotonous sound. The two passengers sitting across from us had not closed their eyes, but they did not appear to be looking at anything at all. The shawl still covered the woman's face like an impenetrable wall, revealing nothing of the world hidden behind it. The train whistle entered the compartment and faded away as quickly as it had sounded. Around me, tired faces were enveloped by invisible fates.

On the horizon, streaks of light had already embraced the colors of the night. The train tracks floated through gray fields with dispersed hues of green. The tracts of land multiplied as the locomotive gained speed. From the cracks of the windows a speck of sea air made its way into the carriage. At first, the odor, unlike that given off by land plants, remained unrecognized. It did, however, force the passengers to open their eyes against their will. "It must be harvest time for some other people," uttered someone in the compartment to our left. A different voice promptly warned him of the danger of unfamiliar odors. "They make you forget the road back home," he admonished. There was no answer.

I glanced at the raindrops fusing with one another on the windowpane until they were swept away by the wind. An even deeper silence had taken over the whole carriage.

My memory fastened upon the Sunday meals my mother ceremoniously prepared once she had gathered from the fields all that others had overlooked in times of harvest. Once sorted out, the yield was set aside and jealously guarded for the long winter. Sunday was a call to gather around the fireplace, where olive tree stumps slowly burned, filling the one-room house with the smell of olives ripened in the month of November. The small flame was the revered source of heat, and the light it gave off was our family's only protection against the night. Brief imaginary harvests were relived through the assortment of the fruit and grains which my mother had found. The salvaged chestnuts, almonds and figs were handled with utmost reverence. Nothing was discarded. "One day you will not feel the shame of picking up what others left behind in the fields." It was Father who said this, his back turned to the fireplace. Not long after, my younger brother and I decided to no longer suffer from want. "We will take what we need and as we please from those who have it," I assured my brother. I knew exactly where every fruit tree grew in Sheshi and the type of fruit it bore. My after-school hours were dedicated to finding what the family needed to lessen our hunger. At times Mother took it as a gift from Divine Providence when she found a small sack of fresh olives which I had taken from their hiding place under the earth of the olive groves and left for her. She never failed to share these gifts with Angelina whose house faced ours and whose limp was familiar to all in the village.

Angelina had been widowed by the last war and then forgotten by her two sons, who left Sheshi convinced they could find black gold in the sunless fields of the Orinoco. I soon came to realize that it was not the olives that Angelina came for, nor the few roasted chestnuts, but news of her two sons from the train when it stopped to fill its belly with water at the station on top of the hill. Mother always gave her the same answer. "The train is late today." Angelina remained unconvinced, for she could hear the rumbling of the locomotive even before it entered the first of the seven tunnels. The only thing she could not detect for certain, at times, was the exact number of carriages that accompanied the locomotive and that was because of the tricks that her eyes played on her.

Morning after morning, Angelina got up hours before the first train was due to arrive. She drank her barley coffee and, without going beyond the time allotted to the alleviating moment of its aroma, she took her seat in front of the dilapidated window and, with her fingers crossed, she waited to hear the distant sound of the train. No one in the vicinity of Angelina's house could say for how long she had been waiting for the one train that would bring back her two sons. But, as the days, the months, and the years went by, and the trees she could see in the distance changed in size and in color, she herself began to wonder at it all and to feel uneasy about her desire to hear the scraping of the train's wheels along the tracks. A painful feeling reverberated inside her breasts. It reminded her of the far away, distressing sensation she had felt during childbirth. She had born three dead children out of five. The last two had been just three years old when their father, in a black uniform and feathered hat, had waved good bye to them with an uncertain smile. Angelina kept looking for that smile until her last breath not long after a fateful day. It had been raining incessantly for thirty-three days when, to her utter amazement, Angelina heard the train stop at the station of Sheshi for a long time. Suddenly, the glass on the photographs of her missing husband and that of her two sons who sought fortune in the high Andes had shattered into dozens of pieces. Although the photographs themselves remained miraculously untouched, her husband's imposing figure in his Fascist uniform and fine hat now bore scratches all over the front left side. Soon after, the cuts began to emit an unmistakable salty odor. It was at that moment that, in a flash of lucidity, Angelina came to realize that the train had stopped to deliver the news of the death of her two sons. She was mistaken.

That day the town's postman took longer that he should have to deliver the letter to Angelina's house. Actually, he could remember neither the name nor the location of the house. He was certain that it was one of the many padlocked houses clothed in vanishing memories that still existed in Sheshi. Perhaps his father with the watery eyes would have known. The postman spent hours with the municipal birth records trying to trace the name of the person on the envelope, now half erased and half eaten by moths. As he worked, the bells of the Church of the Dead began to ring, announcing to the townspeople the death of someone. The postman had made certain that the news of the arrival of the casket at the train station would have reached everyone in the four corners of the village before sunset. Later, he stopped to have a cup of black coffee followed by the usual glass of water at the town's only café. There no one else could trace the name on the envelope to anyone in the village. Yet, each held a vague memory of having seen someone behind the opaque glass of a window while en route to the fields. As time went by and with so many changes in Sheshi, people simply began to think of the old woman as one of the dead who watched over them.

That morning Prefti Vlasë could barely rise from his high wooden bed. He could not move his legs and he coughed convulsively. He had to gather all his strength to call Serafina. "Dust the high altar and the front seats. Make certain you replace the holy water from the font. We are going to celebrate Mass for someone coming home."

Serafina placed some wood on the stove and warmed a cup of black tea for Prefti Vlasë so that his cough might ease before he had to face his parishioners. The holy water in the font had given life to a variety of living things and the smell was so unbearable that it would take months to get rid of it with the help of wild rose petals. Serafina could not recall the last time she had cleaned the marble font, and that made her a bit uneasy. "One never knows how things move outside this church anymore," she sighed as she scrubbed the outer ridge. "It would be a great help if I could rely on something else to remind me of the day of the week instead of trusting the hardly audible sound of the train." What Serafina missed most was seeing the children playing outside the main entrance to the church and sitting on its cool steps in the hot afternoons. She would gaze at their faces from the door left ajar for that purpose, and, through their smiles and manners, she would recall the memories she had stored of their grandparents. At times she had to wait for days to see the children play outside the church. In their absence, she recalled the moments of the distant past when the young ones of Sheshi had been so close to her.

It was in November. For the entire month of October they had been busy making white candles from bits of pork lard which had been saved under oil throughout the previous year during the slaughtering of the family pig. This was the way to close the harvest and to prepare for the coming snows. No one knew nor dared to ask where the children gathered to prepare these candles, but they were exactly the same size and all white so that the angels could see their reflections in the flames as they brought the souls of the dead down from on high to the respective marble tops of their tombs. At this time Sheshi was always enveloped by a thick fog. The café in the square floated in smoke and was cloaked with a heavy aroma of black roasted coffee beans and hand-made tobacco butts. In the streets, just a few lights lit the passageway so as not to confuse the children as to the exact amount of brightness that each candle needed to be seen by the angels.

A few hours before the fog descended from the seven mountains, Aristi had hung dozens of signs inside and outside the café reminding the men to return home before the clock on the town hall tower struck twelve. Each man had carried a lantern and a string attached to the door of his house to avoid getting lost in the fog. For this reason, it was called "the night of the strings." After the final stroke of the midnight hour, the children came out of their hiding places to gather up the strings and to weave cradles with them. The weaving, which was accompanied by beseeching prayers, reminded many of the newcomers to Sheshi, attracted by the descent of the souls from the distant skies, of the times past, which they were struggling to keep alive in the deepest recesses of their memories.

As the town officials made their way up to the station to receive the returned remains of Angelina's husband, the women of the village had been busy placing the children in line with their pockets full of white candles. With stiffened wax wings on their backs, the children led the procession to the Chapel of the Three Crosses midway between the village and the cemetery. There was even a band of eleven men led by the only musician in Sheshi. The sad notes of the music provided some consolation to the grieving men carrying the tiny box. Angelina, however, appeared confounded, unable to make sense of their outpouring of grief. That morning, the train had arrived earlier than usual, forcing all those present at the station to adjust their watches to the exact time. But what had stunned them was the train itself, for no one of them had ever seen a locomotive of its like before. It made no noise and emitted no steam. Times had certainly changed. As the door of one of the carriages opened, a neatly dressed young man in a blue uniform deposited the small wooden box on the platform, boarded the train, and, with the penetrating sound of the whistle he wore attached to a cord around his neck, signaled the conductor to move on.

The train faded into the tunnel as quickly as it had arrived. Angelina, who had witnessed the ceremony with complete composure, lifted the box and held it with both hands. Years later she was to recall the smell of ashes that seeped from the weightless container, bound with shiny strings. Without lifting her eyes from the box, Angelina resolutely began her descent from the station to the Church of the Dead. The town officials who lined the road and the band that followed the cortege were stunned. The elderly widow could not have managed to walk by herself with the box containing the remains of her husband. What they could not see was that the cat's cradles which the children had woven of string were now suspending the box for her. Angelina's feat was a phenomenon destined to have no explanation and to be placed in the register of unsolved mysteries by the town's official recorder of events.

Half way down to the Church of the Dead, Angelina had lost her memory of the place. She was unable to find the thread in the well of her memories. The restoration work done on it and the addition of five more steps to its entrance to make the ascent less arduous for the old people of the village, who could barely lift their feet, made the edifice totally unrecognizable to her. By instinct and by relying on faint remembrances difficult to pinpoint, Angelina took the rocky road that led to the old church carved into the volcanic mount at the edge of the cliff. The icon of the ancient Virgin Mother of Constantinople was adorned with fresh flowers gathered by the guardian of the chapel, a diminutive old man with a white beard and sad eyes. They knelt and whispered together in broken tones a song unfamiliar to the children, who had followed the procession. The young ones, unable to trace the sounds to anything they had ever heard before, listened to the song as a brook finding its way through the rocks and coming to rest amidst the odor of wild basil. And indeed those whose eyes saw far into the horizon now saw basil seeds sprouting from the box which Angelina carried while the incense of burned leaves intensified around her. The widow, tearless and steady, handed the box to the children standing in a circle nearby her.

Quietly, Angelina took the road uphill towards her house. She was followed by the uneven and unsteady steps of an old man carrying a lantern on his wooden cane. The thick fog that had descended from the mountains rendered almost invisible the two silhouettes, one after the other, as they drifted on the same path. Angelina turned around and sent a glance through the wall of fog to her husband, soon to be nourished by the womb of the damp earth. On the heights of the fog, candle lights flickered. Angelina turned again and quickly recognized the old bearded man who had been walking behind her. It was her father. She identified him by his bent back and uneven steps. He had spent many years traveling through winding and disappearing roads to find his way back to the Chapel of the Three Crosses.

Angelina attempted to embrace him and to take hold of his trembling hand. "Why didn't you let me know you were coming?" He tried to harvest the words together to answer but could not remember the order of things. "I have been seeking the house through many winters, but I could not recognize it until the train came to get me," he managed to stutter. "The last carriage stopped at the crossroads of the crooked hill so that I could accompany the thousands of boxes of bones to their resting places."

That afternoon Angelina made coffee for her father as she had done so many times in the past. He drank it with tears in his eyes, recalling the taste of it during those distant early evenings when he would sit on the stone bench in front of the house. "The mule had just been loaded with the fresh fruit and vegetables brought from the fields. The neighborhood children were busy chasing each other before the sun disappeared behind the mountains, and the smell of the evening meal shone in their eyes as they glanced at one another." He had spent many a year struggling to find a way to prevent those memories from withering away. "On that last evening as the church bells rang, I was returning home, directing the mule so as to avoid any stone being caught in its shoe. I saw your grandfather resting on the trunk of an olive tree. Surrounded by hundreds of black birds, he rested his arms on his chestnut cane and looked straight towards

18

me with a distant smile." For the first time in her life, Angelina thought she saw tears in her father's eyes. "At that moment," he went on to say, "I knew that life would never be the same. I slowly lifted myself onto the mule and gently directed the animal to move faster towards home. The old chestnut trees that lined the road had taken on a life of their own and, in their shadow, I sensed, for the first time, the sadness of my isolation. I did not have time to unload the mule. I rested on this stone bench and realized that I could not even turn my head all the way to get a last glimpse of the house. I did take with me the image of the table with the wooden chairs around it. Your mother must have been busy tending the fire and seeing to it that the meal would be on the table even before I unloaded the mule. She did not think to look outside. I remember lowering my head slightly, and the world around me became silent."

Her father's last words brought up long-hidden memories in Angelina. She recalled how that evening, after they had found her father's body slumped on the stone bench, no one had said a word. Little had she known that the little girl, already with the forlorn look of a widow, had been destined to take the reins of the family at a young age. She had worked the fields with her brothers and younger sister as the mother sat day after day, month after month, on the wooden chair, her eyes fixed through the winds and the rains on the road which, to her mind, was to bring back her husband.

One winter morning she closed one eye and left the other open, just in case he would find his way back home. She was buried without receiving the last rites from the town's priest. He was convinced that she was still alive. Many years later, Angelina herself was to relive that distant morning as she herself took her place next to the window waiting for the train to bring back her own husband from the long war. As the years passed, the noise from the tracks became fainter and fainter until the morning the train stopped longer than usual.

To make certain that the old lady would still be there, the postman of Sheshi customarily sat down, once his late afternoon rounds were through and everyone else had left the one-room office, to write his usual letter to Angelina. He simply wanted to keep her alive and to dream of her sparkling eyes. He searched for the right words in an old dictionary and sprinkled them with ashes, ever careful not to betray his feelings. The postman's name was Anisi, and he was the last person in the village who knew of Angelina and who could find the road that led from the post office to the door of her house, which stood beneath her window.

It was not easy for Anisi to get there once a year. It took him days to find the scarcely visible road and months to avoid the alleys that crisscrossed one another and had only one entrance and no exit. Anisi learned to rely entirely on certain faded faces painted in black ink on the stone walls. When merely five, the postman had seen Angelina waving good-bye to her husband with one hand while she held her two children close to her with the other. Hers was the face Anisi remembered the day darkness fell upon him. The black lines on the wall blackened further as he turned from one alley into another, and it did not take long for the postman to realize that the faces were actually still alive. Afterwards, the postman did not share his discovery with anyone. He took it with him even after he finally succeeded in finding his way to the other side of the painted walls. Anisi's whole existence had become obsessed with his need to deliver those letters to Angelina. The process had become so routine that only the people accustomed to receiving their mail at a certain hour as usual became suspicious of the delays. With time, the delays became more frequent and the delivery more disorderly. Some began to receive their mail even during the night. "Don't blame it on me," Anisi would reply to their reproaches. "Petition the town officials to retouch those black faces on the walls of each alley, so that I can find my way out of them more easily, without having to deal with so many additions and subtractions."

With that answer, the whole village became convinced that Anisi had fallen into the trap of mixing numbers and was unable to find his way out of the imaginary maze. "It is time to give the postman other responsibilities," answered the mayor in response to the one thousand signatures on the petition delivered to him by the people of Sheshi one morning as he entered the café and saw them discussing the affair. The fact of the matter was that those people present at the meeting had no recollection of the postman at all. After much rambling, they had not been able to agree on what he looked like or even where he lived. But most had signed the petition to avoid being inconsiderate of the town's elders and out of a desire to continue on with their card games.

Indeed, the mayor himself soon after had to look through boxes of old photographs to recognize and identify those who had delivered the petition for the postman's dismissal. The next morning, immediately after his usual cup of dark coffee and two dried figs, the mayor, with the petition in hand, walked straight to the post office. Wearing as firm a look as he could muster, he firmly announced to the postmaster: "I have here a petition signed by the citizens of this town demanding that you dismiss the postman at once for failing to deliver the mail at the proper hour." The postmaster looked a bit puzzled but not surprised. "Mr. Mayor," he replied, "we no longer deliver mail to people's houses. Machines that light up with different colors fill the screen with messages and deliver them before we even have time to think about it. The last man to deliver the mail sits right there next to the cast iron stove. I myself cannot recall the date of the last mail delivery." Floored by that response, the mayor directed his eyes towards the minute figure of a man who sat like a cricket next to the stove. He had to search through many layers to look into the mirror of his eyes to realize that he had never seen that image of a man before.

Rushing home, the mayor spent the next four years looking among the piles of memorabilia that had been left by his great- grandmother for the photograph which would identify the last of the postmen, he with the mirrors in his eyes. With the patience of a watchmaker, he set aside those photographs that most resembled the old man. Wrapping them carefully in thin paper, the mayor went down to the ends of the village to consult with its two eldest people. They were sisters...indeed, identical twins. They were similar in every detail but for a birthmark on the left earlobe of one of them. The twins guarded this secret day and night. Each took turns, every two hours, to defend the birthmark from the ravages of time. A fresh basil leaf grown expressly for this purpose was applied on the discoloration before sunrise and after sunset. The mayor knew through inaccessible memories that he was in the right house. "An irresistible aroma of basil will lead you to their home," his bed-ridden mother had told him before he left the house.

It was a rainy day. It had rained for days, making the descent down to the homes carved from the volcanic deposits at the bottom of the village difficult and uncertain. The streets became narrower and more tortuous, with each winding into the next ever more confusedly, particularly since each street looked very much like the previous ones. In his hurry, the mayor had forgotten to take down the lantern from its customary spot on the wall of the dispensary. The distant howling of the dogs roaming through the village filled him with deep, lacerating fears. But the flies buzzing so close to his ears between the raindrops urged him to go on.

His mother had told him to look for a house carved from pink volcanic stone and surrounded by a perpetually green garden. Holding his photographs tightly in the inside pocket of his coat and led by a flock of yellow-breasted birds, the mayor found himself in a well-lit open space lined with almond trees. He barely recognized the cone-shaped green leaves laden with dust because the incessant rains had turned their veins into rivers of tears. But he shortly became aware of the centenarian cries that found their way out of the deep fissures of the earth. At that moment he remembered having heard, while sipping his coffee in the café and paying little attention, of the ageless trees that grew at the end of the village. Now a strange force kept him from getting close to the center of the open space. He could not feel the pebbles beneath his feet, nor could he hear the usual irregular heartbeat that pounded in his chest. "Is this what they mean by death?" he asked himself. And, in fact, he had reached the road where all roads become one.

Awakened from their unison dream by the presence of the stranger, the sisters put on their mantles and tried to open the door to their cave. This was not possible to do by hand. They had to break the rusted lock with a hatchet only to find a second, heavier lock which their father had placed on the outside before he had set out on horseback to reclaim his lost childhood. Peering through the hole left for air in the front wall, the twin sisters saw the stranger as lifeless as a freshly cut tree branch. "Touch the almond tree with your fingers," they advised.

The mayor felt the weight of their voices opening the veins of his body and, with an uncontrolled lazy movement, his arm lifted until he touched the wet bark. At that moment every stone on the road took its own place. The door to the cave opened effortlessly and the two sisters, hardly able to stand, muttered a few unintelligible sounds. "We have been waiting for you," they said together in one voice. But the mayor could not make sense of their greeting. "Have we changed so much in this village?" he pondered as he struggled to hold on to the smile he had directed at the two women. In their chain of years, the sisters had devised their own line of communication and had never tested it out on anyone outside their home.

The mayor, realizing the futility of fusing his own sounds with those of the twins, proceeded to show them the neatly arranged photographs that held the untold events of the founding of Sheshi. The photographs brought to life the images of the people watching the twins' father dig into the earth and plant the first almond seed. "I shall come back to the village when the tree will bear its first fruit," he had told the crowd. "And I shall send word through the copper wires hiding high among the trees. There is one among you who shall harvest the message inside the chestnut grove and will let it be known to the rest of the people."

He was referring to a young child, just three years old, balancing upon his father's shoulders. That child began the search for the unwritten word as soon as he was able to make sounds and words inseparable from each other. From that moment on, the child was called "Anisi." At a tender age, he had already filled his corner space at the house with all kinds of signs carved into the volcanic stone wall.

24

At night the signs moved in and out of his mind, always looking for different considerations. The windows remained tightly shut, the doors locked and every crack in the walls sealed so as not to lose any of the sounds. A few years later, Anisi discovered without fanfare a way to trap the sounds running from inside the copper wire playing hide and seek among the tree tops. He transferred the sounds on a golden needle that tapped invisible words on a silver plate. Anisi gave his discovery a name..."telegraph"...explaining to the people of the village that the word meant "crooked lines" and that their origin was from somewhere beyond the seven mountains.

Soon Anisi's corner space inside the one-room home was proclaimed a shrine revered for connecting the village with the unseen world beyond the mountains, and Anisi was acknowledged to be the sole interpreter. This was the birth of the post office. Shortly thereafter, a row of almond trees was planted to provide shade for the hundreds of people who daily lined up to receive news from their loved ones. Mothers washed and cooked outside their homes waiting to hear the first sounds of the silver plates that would bring any sign that their sons and husbands in far away lands were still alive. It was then that Anisi decided, with much difficulty, to deliver the messages directly to their homes as he received them.

At first Anisi spent hours decoding and interpreting the messages for the women. But this soon became too great a task as messages began to fill the silver plate with greater speed and an increased sense of urgency. Anisi wasted no time in sharing the secrets of the sounds and their many combinations with all the mothers in the village. He did not bother to summon the men. They were too busy in the fields, clearing the land for seeding and dreaming of the biggest harvest ever. Besides, Anisi knew that plants had another system of sounds that could not be mingled with those inside the copper wires.

Among the women who attended the regular midday gatherings with Anisi was Anastasia, the mother-to-be of the twin sisters. But she rarely paid attention to his explanations of the minute details of sound formations. Instead, her mind floated out of the house of the copper wires, through the ceramic tiles, and ended up on the bell tower of the old church on top of the hill, where many years later, unbeknownst to anyone in the village, the first train was to pass. Anastasia came to realize that inside the bells lay the secrets of those sound arrangements. She wasted no time in sharing her discovery with the begetter of the telegraph. "How is it that things are always revealed by chance?" Anisi exclaimed to himself. Yet, he himself was in no hurry to share Anastasia's findings with anyone else. Indeed, he dismissed her from the group for being inattentive and given to reverie. "Go and play house in the fields of clay below the hill of the three dolls," he admonished.

It was in these multicolored clay slopes that Anastasia returned to her childhood. Day after day, her fingernails bleeding, she scooped out the clay needed to build houses with unending rooms and cherry-colored furniture. She even contrived to build a dollhouse similar to one she had heard of once, although she could not recall exactly where or when. In just a short time, without anyone's noticing, Anastasia perfected the art of making clay figurines. She was even able to violate the laws of gravity, for some of them stood erect, others leaned to the left or the right, and still others lay all flat in the air. Anastasia relived her childhood in and out of the bamboo dollhouse until one day she could no longer hide within the hollow stems. Instead she found herself on the bell tower of the church on top of the hill by simply closing her eyes.

It came to pass one early afternoon, while she was setting the clay figurines directly under the sun so as to dry them naturally, that a raggedy-shaped man, approached, moving with great difficulty and leaning on a knotted cane. He sat on a stone stool of the house and asked for a bowl of water. Anastasia turned at once toward the clear, discerning voice and was amazed to see the image of an uncertain face. Behind the stranger's eyelids she saw all her figurines dancing with bouquets of flowers in both hands. Anastasia's entire body went into convulsions, with every bone resetting into its proper place. In the morning Anastasia awoke to find herself in the last corridor of womanhood.

The two spent much of the winter waiting for the high winds to abate. And as the first sign of green appeared on the eastern side of the horizon they loaded the mule with all the figurines neatly packed and set out to reach the small settlement of Albanians on the other side of the blue ridge. The long arduous climb through the narrow mountain passes and the cold temperature of midnight broke into countless pieces all of the delicate figurines, with the exception of two. These Anastasia had placed in a sack between her breasts because they would not fit with the rest. It was there, sustained by the warm milk dripping from Anastasia's swollen breasts, that the two figurines began to look for the rays of the sun. Bewildered, Anastasia asked her guard how this had come to pass, but the old man, now more a shadow than an image, gave no answer. Anastasia cared for the two inquisitive figurines with all the tenderness of a young mother. And in their many years of traveling around the seven mountains, scorched by the midday sun, buffeted by the evening winds, or soaked by nightly downpours, they never lost hope of finding the promised cave that led to the Albanian outpost.

It was, in fact, through their few glimpses of the moon that they counted the months and the years. These they recorded with a twist of a knife in the bark of a giant fig tree carefully guarded from the inclemency of the seasons by two curved mountain slopes. At times the travelers felt they were moving in circles, for both seemed to remember a spot even before they reached it. But neither could be totally certain, because the colors of the tree leaves kept changing with the flow of the wind.

"I shall dig for the cave under that ant hill," the old man told Anastasia as they rested under a cypress tree. It brought Anastasia relief to hear him speak for the first time since she had seen him that remote afternoon when she had been unable to tell whether he was a child or a grown man. She immediately traced the sounds that had emanated from his mouth to those she heard from the bells of the chapel on top of the hill in Sheshi.

With the cave carved from the volcanic ridge with an entrance and an opening at the top, the old man and Anastasia began to feel like a family. A small wheat field along the winding brook basked beneath the afternoon sun. Day after day Anastasia gathered everything she could find and added them to the picket fence she busily built during the night. It was to guard the perpetual vegetable garden from everything around except the sun and the frozen raindrops which came without warning. Without the knowledge of the old man, Anastasia thought of sharing the secret of the sound from the church bells with her two figurines, whom she called "my twin daughters."

It was not long after that the old man realized that the women were communicating in a language unknown to him.

Without making an effort to decipher the strange sounds, he decided to prepare his departure. He felt an indefinable pain, one he had never before experienced, which made knots in his throat. He walked to the wheat field along the brook, took the almond seed from beneath the moist earth and summoned everyone from the four horizons to his side. "I shall leave with the early rays of the eastern sun to search for the well that nourishes the sounds of the bell tower on top of the hill, and I shall return when this almond seed shall grow into a tree and bring forth its first fruit. Listen to the sounds inside the copper wires, for in them my homecoming shall be announced." Among those in the crowd, their heads lowered and filled with fright, there was one child whose innocent smile was to accompany his never ending search for the origin of sound.

The mayor had listened with stupefaction to this story told in perfect harmony by the twin sisters. He felt the need to go back to the post office and converse with Anisi in the language he had heard from the twins. Outside the cave-house dusk had settled on the almond tree as the black crows kept watch over the valley from the chimney tops. The mayor of Sheshi could not remember ever having walked with such ease as he effortlessly found his way out of the maze of streets by following the hundreds of lanterns that illuminated his way back to the main square. The air was filled with a conundrum of perfumes fast climbing from the trees in bloom in the valley below. The unseasonable sweet breeze had already invaded the open spaces of the houses of Sheshi. The ancient fountain in the main square hummed with the chatter of the women busy with their evening wash. But amidst the festive atmosphere of the square and his own indescribable inner tranquility, the mayor could not make his presence felt in the place. He tried in so many ways to call their attention, but to no avail. "How is it that they neither see me nor feel my hand when I touch them?" he asked. He tried to scream next, but no sound came from him. When he embraced them one by one, no one felt his touch. The mayor knew then that he was a stranger in the village. And what gave further verification to this realization was his waiting in vain for the sun to set. It stayed immobile right above the square, where thousands of white butterflies flew about, and it neglected to seek a place to set on the other side of the seven mountains. "This is a strange way to come to the end of the road," he tried to whisper to himself. He had not even taken leave of his mother, nor had he even had time to place the winter blanket across her knees.

The first and only person in the village who became aware of the mayor's death near the cave of the almond tree that bloomed with every season of the year was Aristi, the owner of the café. He did attempt to warn the mayor's mother, but could not find the entrance to the road that led to her house behind the faded faces on the walls. It was not long after that that the body was found, lying as if asleep at the entrance to the cave. The two young shepherds who came upon it thought at first that the person was a stranger who, caught by the late hour of the night, had fallen asleep on the stone bench enveloped by a viscous sheet of fog. To the rest of the villagers, the mayor's death came as no surprise. For a long time he had not been a part of them. And they had known that it was just a matter of time before he would be unable to recognize the road that led to the village square. Sheshi had fallen prey to long and bitter winters with less and less wood to burn in the hearths.

Through the empty spaces left by the fallen raindrops on the window of the train compartment, I saw the smoke from the distant chimneys climbing lazily towards the clouds.

"The clouds are God's cradles filled with sleeping angels," Mother used to murmur as we cozily sat around the burning olive log over which the evening meal slowly simmered in its terra cotta pot. As I looked at Mother, who had not moved at all across from my seat, I could see the dark blue flow of the blood through her veins. How impenetrable those people who sat in that small space were at first glance. Each was locked in his own world, locked forever in a timeless, unreachable place that no endeavor could unfold. That interior world was their only line of defense against the dense darkness outside. It was in the pleasantness of the fireplace that I began to stitch together, one by one, the beads of my memories and tie them with the warmth that emanated from the burning log and the silent loneliness of the train tracks.

Chapter Two

The heavy breathing of the great-grandmother mingled with the howling wind sneaking in through the cracks of the weather beaten wooden door as she stretched the virgin wool freshly shaved from the belly and back of the sheep. In the corner near the stable and the fireplace sat the head of the family. It was the place he took evening after evening, especially during the winter months when the fields slept, gathering their strength for the coming spring. There he sat, white woolen fez over his head, carving a cane with his moon-shaped knife. Great-great-grandfather Ndre Frushtari carried a heavy weight on his shoulders. He had been carrying it since that fine April morning when his father, Kristo Frushtari, first called him by his given name. It was a heavy burden and one that Ndre Frushtari was to take to his grave, so people said, for it could be seen on the daguerreotype placed on his marble tomb. From his place in the corner he maintained an avowed silence, focusing all his attention upon working the moon-shaped knife on the cane. During the winter months he carved dozens of canes of different sizes and shapes, leaving them to dry on the front wall of the fireplace.

Ndre Frushtari's story was sung throughout the four corners of Sheshi and perhaps even beyond the seven mountains. The oldest of the storytellers of the village maintained that the event that was to change the life of Ndre Frushtari happened during the harvesting of the olives between fall and winter. It was during the early days of November. The rain had begun to fall lightly over the olive groves. The women of the village had descended into the fields to begin carefully picking the black olives without breaking the tender branches. The olive groves sent silver rays into the sky. The young filled the air with enchanting songs, hoping to lure the olives from their hiding places between the silver leaves. The older women thought of the golden liquid gushing out of the crushed olives soon to fill the empty jars.

For Ndre Frushtari, soon to come of age, no preparations had been made. He only expected a handshake from his father, Kristo Frushtari, and the chestnut cane promised to him by his maternal grandfather, Mitrush Bey. Fall had come and gone and winter had settled in the house with a cloudless morning. The trees, already stripped of their few remaining leaves, reminded Ndre Frushtari of the desolate winter days that lay ahead. Kristo Frushtari, without looking into his son's eyes and with as firm a voice as he could muster, asked Ndre Frushtari to dress warmly and to pick up the shotgun that he had placed on the kitchen table. A deeply hidden fear took possession of the boy's body. He fastened himself to the chair with both hands so as not to shame his father. Now Ndre Frushtari understood why in the dream during the night he had not been able to find his way back home from the olive grove after he had filled the wicker baskets with olives and had set them in a circle under the trees.

"It is time for you to avenge your sister's honor," Kristo Frushtari said to his son with his eyes fixed on the burning log in the fireplace. Ndre Frushtari understood immediately what was expected of him and said nothing. That morning he carried with him the silent meaning nestled among his father's words, but he was not yet aware that he would never again look at his father's face. Those solid features that had made him feel so secure as a child during his many sleepless nights would no longer be able to dispel his fears.

After finding the cup of coffee which his mother morning

after morning prepared for him before leaving for the fields, Ndre gathered up the black cape which had been set aside with his scarf and woolen gloves. His older sister, Hanna, handed him a double-knotted cloth with a loaf of bread, cheese and a handful of dried olives. He wrapped the cape about himself and left the house without uttering a sound, struggling to hold back the tears which scalded his eyes.

The sky had darkened with threatening, quickly moving clouds. Ndre took the outlying alleys of the village, trying to avoid being recognized by any passerby. He was not aware of the many shutters which had been left ajar that morning, as if bidding him goodbye. Behind them, unseen, were the elders of the village who for generations had witnessed the departures of the young. They were caught between the memories of the past and the sense of uselessness of their old age. At the window of the last house at the end of the village Ndre saw the pallid visage and scarcely visible smile of Bardha, who was waving a black piece of cloth. She had waited for hours that morning to wave to him, for she had a strong premonition that it was to be the last goodbye. Bardha had managed to get up from the chair by placing both hands on the window sill. Lifting her left hand to wave the black cloth had taken all her strength away.

Later that afternoon, the house cleaner would find her withered away next to a dry bouquet of white lilies. But on that early morning, Ndre, tormented by an unfamiliar pain in his chest, did not wave back to Bharda. Her reflection behind the window glass had blurred with the passing of a dark cloud over the cobblestone alley. Ndre did not learn of Bardha's death until many years later. He vowed never to love anyone else with the same intensity and itch he felt on his left eye. But what hurt him the most was his regret for not having accompanied her to the gates of the Church of the Three Crosses on the road to the village's cemetery.

The sun, brighter than usual, emerged from the tallest of the seven mountains, but it was quickly engulfed by clouds. Ndre positioned himself at the crossroads between the olive grove and the end of the village. His hand was cemented to the shotgun. A quiet drizzle had begun to fall as he took position behind the olive tree closest to the road. "It won't be long before he will come through here," Ndre murmured to himself. He was afraid of the stiffness in his hand on the shotgun. He hardly remembered Abdil, who had offended Hanna and for whom he now waited. And he lamented his sister's lot, forever locked within the four stone walls of her room.

Ilía was destined never to learn of the death of her son, Abdil; the smile he had saved for her during the long days of winter as he cared for her died within him that early autumn morning. Ndre thought of the news of the killing spreading like wildfire through every house of Sheshi. By evening it would be the talk of the village in the square of the old fountain and at Aristi's café.

Ndre's father, Kristo Frushtari, had raised the members of his family with the strictest rules concerning their honor. He was not about to break rules which had been handed down to him by his father and grandfather. Kristo Frushtari had promised both that he would never deviate from those legacies. Ndre thought of how little he knew his father. Theirs had been a fixed relationship, set down by laws that had governed Sheshi since the time of the first memories. Gripping the grille of the shotgun even more tightly, Ndre could not recall ever having gone against his father's wishes. Kristo Frushtari's imposing look and unwavering posture left no space for anyone to argue with him. He ruled the household with an iron fist, signaling with glances, not words. Ndre could count on his fingers the few words his father exchanged with his grandfather during an evening meal.

"I shall leave for the fields before sunrise," Kristo Frushtari had told his wife the night before he handed his shotgun to Ndre Frushtari. "There is plowing to be done."

On that day Elena Musa fixed her eyes on the road that her husband had taken to reach the fields. The fog had cloaked half of the village and the drizzle had erased the lines of the road. Elena Musa had begun to put the house in order and to prepare the evening meal. She set aside the bowl with water for her husband to wash his hands and face. The two-room house with the fireplace on the same wall as the door smelled of cooked beans and lard. This was the familiar evening smell in Sheshi.

While he waited for Abdil to appear, Ndre smelled once more the aroma of the cooked beans in the fireplace. He saw his mother placing the dishes on the table and setting the hard round bread in the middle of it. "Did she know what Father ordered me to do this morning?" he asked himself. He would have expected at least a greeting from her that morning, but Elena Musa had not even turned her face to him. She had just continued with scrubbing, albeit a little harder. Ndre did not dare to address her in his father's presence. "I could have told her of the pain in my knees, deep inside the bones, tearing them apart."

Now Ndre's breathing grew heavier and heavier. The cold, incessant drizzle hit his face, numbing his cheeks. "I shall get it over with as quickly as I can," he vowed with his teeth chattering uncontrollably. "The important thing is not to graze him. I must aim straight at his heart and then run quickly towards the cave of the painted icons." His father had told him to bury the shotgun on the left side of the cave where he had dug a deep hole. "You will see the hole covered with fig leaves and a few olive branches. And do not leave the other bullet in the shotgun." As Kristo Frushtari was closing the door to the house that early autumn morning, he had reminded his son to look for a small envelope inside the hole of the cave of the icons. "In it there is some money that will get you to Naples and then across the great divide. On the other side of the ocean you will find work and people who speak like you. Do not trust anyone. Look deep into their eyes to see the Icon of the Virgin of Constantinople. One day I shall come to look for you. I give you my word."

It was that promise that gave Ndre the strength to lift the shotgun and aim straight for the heart of Abdil, who bent his knees when the bullet penetrated his heart and slowly fell into the muddy road. Ndre, breathing heavily, rushed to ascertain that he had not missed the target. He saw Abdil curving his body like a cat. Ndre felt his pain inside his own throat and he smelled the blood gushing out of the wound. Abdil's bulging eyes seemed to ask forgiveness. Then he smiled from far away and, with his mouth open, he let go of his last breath. Ndre was to carry Abdil's suffocated pleas with him across the big ocean and through the unending flatlands of the Orinoco. Not one night would come to an end without his reliving the sound of the bullet searching for Abdil's heart and the sadness that covered his face. The report of the shotgun was like a hammer hitting Ndre's head; it was like the bite of a yellow viper in the heat of summer.

The night of the killing had turned bitterly cold. The continuous drizzle turned into ice as it hit the ground. Ndre waited for the train inside the waiting room, where it was pitch dark. Seeing no one on the platform, the station master had not turned on the lights. Fearful of being recognized, Ndre lifted both lapels of his coat. He stepped onto the deserted platform and felt the razor-sharp wind that was quickly descending from the mountain. That night the cold kept everyone at home in Sheshi, which was just as well, since Ndre could not have anyone see him. He moved behind the pomegranate tree, which still bore leaves, and waited. Finally the train came out of the tunnel as if it had been detained by the icy wind. Ndre boarded the last carriage, and then looked from the window to make certain that no one had gotten on the last evening train with him. By then people had come from every corner of the village to the café to get a clearer sense of the event. The howling of the sheep dogs at the far end of the village was carried from house to house by the blustery winds. A cold sweat invaded Ndre as he sat at the far end of the carriage compartment. He started to tremble all over, yielding to his fear.

Ndre had never been out of the village. As a child in the town's barber shop, he had heard the old men speak of the city of Naples. He recalled how he had struggled to make sense of their descriptions and to envision the city streets, the long docks of the seaport that reached into the center of the bay and the ships anchored on each side of it, under a carpet of multicolored lights. He thought of Ramiz, the white-bearded old man who sat for hours outside the barber shop, telling how he had sailed on one of those large ships. "You could only move ten feet at a time inside the ship to avoid getting lost. From the deck of the ship, constantly slapped by wet winds, to the hull were countless cubicles, and in each one there were four beds, one on top of the other, smelling of clean white sheets," recounted Ramiz to anyone who came to sit next to him. Ndre had drawn closer and closer to Ramiz so as not to miss anything. "Then," Ramiz added daily, when the hour on the silver watch he carried in his front vest pocket reached five o'clock in the afternoon, "the boat turned into a great fish and sailed into the night between the stars and the ocean, jumping from one wave into another just as the clouds do when they come down from the seven mountains into the fields of Sheshi."

Ndre, alone and still trembling from the cold and his wet clothes, would have given anything to find himself again in the barber shop listening, his heart pounding, to Ramiz's late afternoon conversations about the city on the other side of the mountains. But the feeling of awe and fascination with which Ndre returned home day after day, after putting the scissors in order and sweeping the floor of the barber shop, was now replaced with a feeling of uncertainty and with an unidentifiable fear. At that moment, Ndre understood the sense of separation from things which he had felt when he had visited his great-uncle, who looked out of the balcony waiting for the sun to set behind the smallest of the seven mountains.

The train conductor passed by the corridor, but he did not ask Ndre for a ticket. He did not seem suspicious at all. He was much more concerned about getting information on the state of the tracks further ahead, between Potenza and Battipaglia. "Have you heard from the station master in Potenza?" he asked the man who had been walking behind him with a lantern in his left hand.

"Not a word, but I would be cautious on the crossroad of the five bridges. The earth there is prone to give way after a few days of heavy rains," the other replied.

The conductor moved ahead, leaving behind the lantern's yellow glow, which faded slowly in the cold air. "I did not even have time to look into my mother's eyes," Ndre thought once more. She had been taking care of the dishes and had not turned around, but she did see his reflection on the glass window. Her heart had pounded against her chest, raising a lump in her throat. She was losing another of her children to an ancient dark force that exacted heavy retribution. "Put your cape on, the air is chilly and wet this morning," his sister had managed to tell him in a confused and unsteady voice. Ndre called to mind his father's last words: "Follow the smell of the sea. It is heavy with salt and it will lead you where the long ships dock. Tell them you leave no one behind and you wish to go to the Orinoco region to work. You will be working for the landowner for two full years before you can demand a wage. They need young men like you, but do not trust the trees. In the savannah, they say, trees talk with one another and breed snakes underneath their roots."

Ndre struggled to keep the information safe in his mind. He had to appear certain and determined to the contractors on the ship. He did not want the officials to see Abdil's agonizing death in his eyes. "I told Abdil to forgive me with a soft whisper in his ear. I realized then that it was not up to him to grant a pardon with that forlorn look that had already settled upon his trusting smile." Little did Ndre know that Abdil had actually longed for years for that moment to be released from his tormenting wait. Perhaps, had Kristo Frushtari known about Abdil's anguish, he might have decided not to send Ndre to take his life as payment for dishonoring his home.

"I will write to Abdil's mother through Bardha," muttered Ndre to himself. "She will read the letter with the colors of her eyes to Ilía Nati." From her rocking chair placed outside the front entrance to her house, Ilía Nati used to watch Ndre and Bardha as children running after their black dog. Vases of geraniums lined both sides of the steps, and a small lemon tree exuded its entrancing scent into the street. The people from the south end of Sheshi purposely chose that street to reach the square of the ancient fountain so that they could breathe in the lemony aroma. Ilía Nati rarely moved from where she sat. She just stayed there from morning until dusk waiting for Abdil to return home and sit next to her. People waved at them as they passed by, but only Abdil returned the greetings.

No one knows how it happened, but one clear spring day, Adbil's mother simply could not select her images anymore. Ilía Nati sat on the rocking chair and began to follow the scent of the flowers carried on the soft spring breeze. Abdil went to the entrance of the village to summon the soothsayer, her hair braided into a long single plait. "No," she asserted the minute she saw Abdil in front of her cave dwelling, "she is not dying. She has gone back to where she came from." But no one in the village could help Abdil trace that place.

Long ago Ilía Nati had come to Sheshi with an old suitcase tied crossways with a rope. She had been sitting on the wooden bench of the train station for a long time before the station master noticed her after the train had left the station. "Are you waiting for someone to pick you up?" he asked Ilía Nati in gentle tones. She seemed frightened and pale to him, more a child than a grown woman. She wore a shawl around her head and about her neck. "I was told by the train conductor to get off at this station and to wait for the person whose name appears on the envelope," said Ilía Nati without lifting her eyes towards the tall figure of the train master. He saw the envelope in her hand and attempted to read the name written there, but she would not let go of it. "He will know when to come for me," she mumbled, still not lifting her head. "I will have to wait until dusk; the moonlight will direct him to me."

The trainmaster noted the strong determination in her words, but at the same time he could not help smelling the look of sadness descending from her eyes. It seemed that

Ilía Nati had traveled for many years searching for the village her grandmother had spoken to her about. "It is a place where the almond trees in bloom carpet the whole countryside and where the wind in late fall cradles the black swallows inebriated by the sound of the church bells."

Puzzled by the presence of the woman, the station master forgot to retrieve the mail sack left on the tracks and to turn off the bell on the front wall of the station. Ilía Nati's apparition had upset his balance between the day and the night. He bid her good day and rushed to his private room to look into the corner mirror next to the flowering plants. The station master shivered all over, for the face he was seeing reflected in the old octagonal mirror was that of his childhood. In the mirror, he was still wearing his dark school uniform with a white collar patiently crocheted by his mother in the hot summer afternoons. He sensed the same separation from his mother as he had felt on his first day of school. How strange it was for the station master that he was no longer concerned about checking the clocks that hung in the room, each set to the arrival of the trains. He felt free of the countless additions and subtractions needed to calculate the exact time. Even the oldest chestnut trees he saw daily from his window did not sway with the afternoon breeze. He put his state railroad hat on and went down to the main office to alert the next station of the railroad line of the stillness in his own station. He reached the front door and attempted to push it open, but it moved away from him, making it difficult to take hold of the knob. He pushed the door itself with all his strength only to find another door behind it. He realized that he was trapped inside the cubicle of time and would never succeed in finding his way out through the tunnel of doors.

Days later, the station master, whose name died with Ilía

Nati that early morning, was found dead by Adbil's father, Ymer Ramat, who had read the instructions of how to reach the train station. Those orders were found written in the letter held by the frail passenger whom he came to fetch at sunset.

"He is to be buried on the east side of the cemetery, next to his mother," Ilía Nati told Ymer Ramat as he led the mule down the rocky road toward his house. The letter, placed in an envelope and filled with flower seeds, had been written by Abdil's father's friend, with whom he had fought in the long war inside the icy trenches that seemed never to be free of snow. "I am sending my youngest daughter to you along with all the flower seeds I could gather as we walked back from the snow fields of the steppes. She will keep you company and will take care of the garden for you." The letter was signed "Ortensi Nati."

Ymer Ramat took good care of Ilía Nati for she often reminded him of her father. They had walked many a mile together sharing the fear, the cold and the confusion of the war until they simply had forgotten who the enemies were. "Yes, war is a terrible thing," Ortensi had often told Ymer as they huddled together under the woolen army blanket, "because you don't know why you are told to kill." Many times, after the war, Ymer Ramat recalled the night when the soldiers in black uniforms had come to take him along. They had driven for three nights and three days before they could find Sheshi. Ymer Ramat found himself in the company of so many people who could barely understand one another. It was then that he had met Ortensi Nati, much older than he, with a forehead full of wrinkles and almond-shaped eyes. Their duty as soldiers was to relay messages from one trench to another. They never did have a chance to look directly into the eyes of any other soldiers, who just stood there motionless, their boots sunk into the mud and their hands cleaved to their guns.

As the war dragged on, Ymer and Ortensi began to notice that on the other side of their trenches there was no one to receive the messages. "Just leave them on the table," they were told. "Someone will come by to read them."

One night, under a moonless sky, they could not find their way back to their compound through the trenches, which seemed to have multiplied. In them, the mud and the stench from coagulated blood covered every possible indicator of the way back. "I think everyone has gone away," said Ortensi. "Tomorrow at daybreak, we shall walk away from this stench and search for the road that will take us back home."

And so it came to pass that early the following morning, as soon as the sun had crystallized the snow, Ymer and Ortensi gathered whatever food and water canteens they could find and, without stepping on the frozen bodies, half-ice and half-mud, they walked toward the horizon where the sun had risen. At night they slept inside the still warm bodies of the dead horses. The road back was filled with soldiers who did not have time to scream.

"There is nothing more precious and at the same time more dispensable than one's life," Ortensi Nati reminded Ymer Ramat as they stopped at midday, trying to harvest the water dripping from icicles. Quite often, Ymer Ramat did not understand Ortensi Nati, but he realized that his companion saw in things what he himself could not see. Thus, Ymer followed and obeyed Ortensi in everything, lending his youthful strength to his friend's efforts to find the way back home.

The two walked for weeks, months, and years feeding on every root Ortensi could find. Many a time they had to hide from other wandering soldiers whom they could not identify as friend or foe because all their uniforms had become indistinguishable. All these men were escaping an invisible pursuer in the snowy fields, one which made terrible noises as they drew closer and closer to the front lines.

Once an old farmer found Ortensi and Ymer sleeping in his barn underneath his two cows and realized immediately that they were not the enemies of his people. They were part of that company of soldiers whom he helped to bury with a smile on their faces. He fed the wanderers with the little he could scratch from under the earth. They spoke very little, mostly through gestures, that night, and in the morning, the farmer hid them in his cart under a pile of freshly cut wood and helped them to cross the river.

There, on that late afternoon, Ortensi and Ymer saw the long line of soldiers, all without weapons, being ferried from one side of the river to the other on makeshift boats. "The war is over," whispered Ortensi. Ymer did not answer for fear of having misunderstood. He simply grasped Ortensi's hand and held it tightly in his own. It was at that moment that Ymer relived his old desire of having a son. "Now you can go back home and start your own garden, and when you are able to produce enough in all the four seasons, you may even think of having a family."

Ymer Ramat never forgot those words, and as soon as he got back to his village he began to save as much as he could so that one day he could have his own vegetable garden and even search for a companion. Ymer never lost hope that his one-time war friend would cross the seven mountains to visit him. And so, when they came to his field to summon him to the train station, Ymer knew that it was Ortensi who had arrived to spend his last years with him.

At the train station, Ymer paid no attention to the tiny

woman sitting in the waiting room with the tightly tied suitcase until they exchanged a rapid glance. Then Ymer was startled to see Ortensi's smile and his almond-shaped eyes. Yet, he had time neither to ask her name nor to inquire about her father; she simply handed him the letter she had gripped so tightly throughout her long journey and made preparations to leave with him. Ymer Ramat saw Ortensi's name written on the envelope, but he did not bother to read the contents of the letter. "We can go home now," he told her as he lifted the tiny woman onto his mule. "I shall read the letter tonight as we sit at the dinner table."

Ilía Nati, the youngest daughter of Ortensi Nati, felt a strange pain in her chest as the mule followed the narrow downhill road towards the center of Sheshi. In the distance she saw the half-carved hills, ragged with outcroppings of stones and sand. The air was laden with dust descending towards the village. Here and there scattered trees and prickly bushes struggled to cling to the dry earth. Just beyond a tall pine tree, Ilía Nati could see the village, each house embracing the other and at times even sharing the same red-tiled roof and the same chimney. Only the crisp red tiles distinguished the roof tops from the whiteness of the horizon. It was then that Ilía Nati understood why her father had given her the sunflower seeds. "Take good care of them," Ortensi had told her. "They will make you feel less lonely."

Ilía began to feel dizzy as the road became steeper. A strange inner trembling had settled in her spine, but she tried to dismiss it. "It is probably from the long trip," she thought. At that point she could not know that the pain would one day climb up through her back and settle right behind her neck. That happened when the dust from the gravel pits settled firmly on the morning dew, slowly withering all the sunflowers that Ilía gently planted and watched growing in pots on the steps leading to her new home.

Ilía Nati's arrival in the village filled everyone with childlike curiosity. Her beauty, they commented, was a field of red poppies intensely reflected against the yellow wheat fields that surrounded Sheshi. The town's one schoolteacher took his pupils to the front door of Ilía's home just to observe the different colors that emanated from her face. The inhabitants of Sheshi were convinced that they had been sent an angel.

Ilía Nati began to shine even more brightly from a distance. When caught by nightfall, the villagers followed that shiny glow nestled on the town's tallest hill to return home. No longer did they fear being swallowed by the darkness. People walked boldly through the streets, feeling sheltered by the light. The old men sitting on the wooden benches of the village square smoked their pipes at late hours while watching the children chasing lightning bugs. At a special town meeting called by the elders to discuss the strange illumination bursting forth from Ymer Ramat's house and saturating everyone who gazed at it with vigor and strength, they decided unanimously to rename the village. "From now on," decreed the nine elders, "the village will be known to our people and to all the strangers passing by as 'Dili Sheshit.'('The Sun of Sheshi')"

Ilía Nati became even brighter and more ethereal as she approached her ninth month of pregnancy. The road that came from behind the seven mountains filled with strangers coming from near and far, even from places whose names had hitherto been nothing more than locations mentioned around the fireplace during the long winter nights. The travelers set up their tents wherever they could find an empty space. Some even brought with them their farm animals.

The women, especially, wanted to be present at the birth of Ilía's child. They recounted daily their own experiences in delivering babies, with the hope that someone would ask them for their help. They even lined up to expose their breasts, swollen with milk and ready to be suckled by the hungry newborn.

Never before, for as long as anyone could remember, had there been so many strangers with so many ways of speaking and dressing camped around Sheshi. Their presence assured everyone in the village that other people, different from them, actually lived beyond the seven mountains and the distant blue horizon. Sheshi was to change forever with everyone caught in its vortex. The dreams that old Viti daily recounted to his friends sitting under the warm sun in the village square as they waited for the children to come and swirl around them was no longer the fanciful story to which everyone had listened halfheartedly in order not to offend him. "In my dreams," Viti related, "I see a sandstorm rushing down from the seven mountains with an enormous fireball of light clearer than the light at dawn. Its rays blind everyone and the doors to the homes are shut. The eyes finally recede into the darkness to avoid total blindness."

The people who daily sat next to Viti thought that he was getting ready to search for the blue horizon on the other side of the seven mountains. But days went by and Viti continued to occupy the same seat on the wooden bench and waited for his companions to arrive and for the children to follow the flight of the swallows seesawing with the sound of the church bells until sunset. Not long after, Viti began to walk behind each one of his friends' funeral processions, accompanying them up to the small church carved under the mountain and then to their final resting place.

One clear autumn day Viti found himself sitting all alone

on the square's wooden bench. The few trees that lined the open space in front of the marble fountain had shed all their leaves. A gray cloud enveloped the church bells, and the swallows no longer swirled around them waiting to catch their sounds. Viti thought he would return home and sit next to his fireplace. There he would have time to reorder his pictures, identifying them with a date and a place on the back. Viti had not noticed the light shining more brightly than ever in Ymer Ramat's house.

That night Viti forgot to put out the fire burning slowly in the hearth. He struggled to lift himself up from the small chair his grandfather had built for him from wild sugar canes. Everything inside the house seemed to have switched places, and the copper pots hanging on top of the mantel made strange noises. One of his legs was completely numb by the time he reached the bed and fell supine upon it. The personal objects that had kept him company for so many years as a widower were fading away before his eyes.

At the window pane the lonely figure of his beloved wife was slowly approaching the bed. The sense of guilt and the old secluded pain of that rainy November day he could no longer hide. He recalled the people of the village following in silence behind as he carried the body of his wife with the rope still wound around her neck. Viti had found her hanging from the fig tree, her eyes still open and gentle. The beauty and serenity of her face would remain forever with him as he shared a few tears with her during the long winter nights. He still blamed himself for her death. "I should have known what she was thinking. Why was I so blind to her fears?" Hënza (as he alone called her) no longer had been able to see her five children go hungry. Viti worked long hours, at times late into the night, as a shoemaker. He was a good shoemaker for the people of Sheshi. But to get paid, he would have to wait until the people could sell their yearly harvest of grapes and olives to the merchants who came on the long trains. The people of Sheshi waited anxiously to hear the whistle of the train approaching the station on top of the hill. For weeks, the peasants spoke of nothing else but the money they would get for their fare. The café smelled of smoke and dreams. While sipping their black coffee, the farmers nurtured thoughts of acquiring more land and increasing the yield from the crops. They had heard from the news brought to the village by the copper wires of the demand for wine and oil in faraway places unknown to them. Young men dreamed of having their own family. The ones who seemed to read their dreams better than anyone else were the old-timers who sat by themselves in the corner of the café, careful not to take more space than was needed. They knew full well that too much water under the bridge would wash the bridge away. But this was not the time to diminish the joy of the harvest.

Yes, the train never failed to arrive; but with it also came the autumn rains. The grapes, neatly packed in wooden boxes, were carefully guarded by members of the family who would each take turns in displaying their produce to the faraway buyers. Tall and precisely dressed, the latter moved from box to box, checking each with the dexterity of an old gambler. Surveying each pile took days, and the rains did not stop. The peasants had no inkling that these foreigners, who never addressed them by name nor even looked at them, were deliberately stalling. The crafty buyers delayed just long enough for the grapes to lose their luster; then they offered the meager price per box that shattered all the dreams fastened together in the café. No peasant dared not to go through with the deal, no matter how it disappointed, and the buyers knew all too well that they had left the farmers with no choice.

Only Zelmi, chewing tobacco nervously, listened to the peasants' complaints. He had traveled to the North from where the merchants came, and had lived among them for many years. "Long enough," he reminded those who gathered around him trying to fathom the image of the big cities of the North which he described. "You must learn their tactics and do things the way they do and then fight them with their own ploys. They need our sweet grapes to mix with their own bitter ones."

But the farmers were instinctively afraid. They would think of the worst that could befall them if they were unable to sell their grapes and olives. "Who will feed our children if we refuse to sell them?" Fruitlessly, Zelmi described in detail the necessity of forming a group of responsible leaders who could create and collect funds to provide assistance to the peasants in times of need. He knew that centuries of persecution and enslavement by the big landowners had conditioned the peasants to mistrust anyone who would attempt to make them believe that they could help themselves. Though the talks went on for weeks, they were forgotten as soon as each of the peasants eventually sold his yield, happy, for the time being, that no one would truly starve. "The next harvest will certainly be bigger and better," each promised himself. "Perhaps different buyers will come to the train station offering higher prices for our own sweet grapes."

The anger that filled Zelmi's gut found an outlet only in Viti's shoe shop. "This village is going to rot if these peasants don't stand up to the buyers from the North."

Viti would let his visitor talk without interfering. He knew he was right, but he dared not reveal it to him for fear of creating false hopes in the young man. Zelmi was a distant relative of his wife, and Hënza cared for the young Zelmi as if he were her own son. It was out of respect for her that a few of the peasants would hire him during the harvest.

With the little he earned, Zelmi was able to get through the winter. Spring brought great relief to him. That was when he began to make preparations to cross the big snowy mountains of the North in search of work. He joined hundreds of other men sneaking through the guarded passes late at night and feeding on roots before finding work on the farms of the high mountains. "I was not permitted to leave the farm because I could not be seen by the local authorities," Zelmi would tell Viti years later. "I would do most of the work at night and hide in the barn during the day until dusk."

Viti's eyes filled with tears as he hammered the leather and listened to Zelmi recall the years he had spent away from the village. "Look at us," Zelmi shouted. "We are condemned to live worse than donkeys and to work only to enrich those who already have more than they need!" Hours would go by in these conversations until it was time to close the shop.

"Tomorrow will be another day. Perhaps someone will remember to pay us for the service rendered," Viti would tell Hënza when he returned home with some dried beans and a cup of wheat flour. Viti walked home from his shop smiling at all the passersby with the hope that they would pay for the shoes he had fixed for them. Those who saw the sadness in his eyes gave him whatever they could spare of the food they had saved for the winter. The rain fell gently, filling the streets with the silence of autumn. The lights seen from far away moved soundlessly into the olive groves, searching anxiously for a place to hide.

In the café, Zelmi sat all alone, pretending to read the yearly gazette that had made its rounds for the full four seasons. Boredom and hunger were making their presence felt. Unable to hint at how much he would enjoy spending the night next to Viti's fireplace, he just watched the bartender, who, in turn repeatedly washed the same few cups as he observed Zelmi tending the seeds of loneliness. The latter looked as if he were waiting for someone else to come in, but the cold night and the thick fog were keeping everyone at home. In the corner, Zelmi was pondering his next trip to the North. The village had become too estranged from him, and a sense of disaffection and alienation was taking complete control of him.

Winter had come to stay. The houses, like so many beehives, shut their doors for months. Zelmi could only smell the smoke coming out of the chimneys as it pointed with intentional destruction towards the massive gray clouds. The few books he possessed became his devoted companions. He was careful not to squander the few pieces of wood he had scavenged, so his one-room home was barely warm.

Now the cold reminded Zelmi of those long, icy nights when his mother, seeing how he trembled, begged her neighbor to let her pale little boy sit next to her fireplace. "He won't take much space; he is so frail."

Irena, who could feel the pain in Zelmi's mother's eyes, could not refuse her request. In fact, Irena asked her husband, Aurelio, to build a seat for the little boy from the wild sugar canes that grew along the hidden brook that traversed their plot of land. For years to come, Zelmi kept that chair next to the fireplace along with the two books that Aurelio had given him, commenting "Here, we won't need them where we are going." Those words descended into the realm of memories destined to be kept alive by the clear waters of the underground rivers.

To the rest of the people of Sheshi, the departure of Irena and Aurelio with the few belongings they could claim as their own seemed to have faded away with the passing of each successive winter. Zelmi had been no more than nine years of age when Irena and Aurelio received from their son, who was born with the clearest eyes and glistening red hair, a letter urging them to join him in a place he called Australia. "The land is so wide and has the color of our red grapes. The natives say that there is no end to it because no one of their people has ever seen the horizon," he wrote. "Here there is no snow, plants grow by themselves, and rabbits are as abundant as fireflies in the sultry summer nights."

Love for their only son convinced Irena and Aurelio to undertake the journey on one of the long sailing ships they had seen advertised on the front walls of the town hall. "Come and sail on top of the ocean towards Paradise," read the announcement adorned with strange flowers and fruits being eaten by sheep standing on two legs with their young in pouches growing out of their stomachs. "I have a feeling that in that place we won't have to break our backs to grow our vegetables and fruits. There is so much to have that they even allow the sheep to graze on them." This is what Aurelio repeated to his wife night after night as she struggled to detach herself from all that had been hers and from the memories of her dead relatives. What convinced Irena in the end, however, were not the strange flowers and animals in those colored posters on the wall of the town hall, but a deeply concealed feeling that her son was suffering from loneliness.

Early the next morning, under the thick mist that had descended from the seven mountains overnight, Zelmi accompanied the couple to the train station. He still could feel the wet, penetrating cold of the morning when he embraced them for the last time. The bell on the wall of the station signaling the arrival of the train had opened inner wounds. "Something tells me we won't be coming back to Sheshi any more," Irena whispered in Zelmi's ear as she kissed his cheeks. The inner umbilical cord was torn to pieces. Zelmi felt a deep urge to urinate as his stomach convulsed uncontrollably.

The train moved as quickly into the tunnel as a tear disappears on a dry summer's night. A few years later, while sitting outside the café during the early evening hours, Zelmi learned of Irena's death of an unknown disease. The village priest announced a Mass to be celebrated in her memory the very next day. It was attended by everyone in town. They listened to Prefti Vlasë speak of the terrible sin that some people carry within them that tempts them to desire more than what God has granted them. "Be happy with what our Almighty has bestowed upon you. Do not venture beyond the threshold of your own home, for that is the call of the Devil," he shouted as he stood taller than usual on the wooden pulpit of the Church of the Dead. It was one of those rare occasions that the priest was not drunk with his own reveries. The parishioners were enthralled by his inner voice as he read from the Sacred Book and with trembling hands carefully placed it on the right side of the altar. Many of the women present at the Mass that late afternoon swore by what they held most holy that they had seen a shaft of light descend over the body of Prefti Vlasë in the pauses between the words he read from the Bible.

Rumor had it that Prefti Vlasë had returned to the days of his youth when he had first arrived in Sheshi, his eyes beaming with faith and innocence. Even Zelmi had noticed the changes in the town's priest, but he had attributed them to Prefti Vlasë's desire to unclasp the necklace of time now that Serafina was no longer there to converse with the saints. It had been her habit, as she changed the flowers beneath their statues, to entreat each saint with the same request. "I hope you will let me know ahead of time when I am going to meet my mother so that I can prepare myself for the reunion." Serafina had been knitting her blue quilt with the yarn that each shepherd in Sheshi brought her on Christmas night. She used some of the yarn to make a coverlet for Baby Jesus in the manger of the Nativity scene, and she saved the rest for herself for her long-awaited trip.

When the village women washed and prepared Serafina for public viewing in front of the altar, they noticed the blue cloth glistening with millions of stars, casting a gleam of light on her pale face. Rome declared Serafina a saint in response to a long petition sent to the Holy City from every village who witnessed on every clear night the multiple stars shining like fallen comets on her tomb.

Now Zelmi felt the loneliness lodging permanently in his bones. Sheshi had fallen into a stupor. Prefti Vlasë abandoned his duties as a servant of the Church and went in search of his childhood. One day from the steps of the church, while avoiding the burning heat of the early afternoon, Zelmi saw Prefti Vlasë sneak out of the refectory dressed in shorts and a tee-shirt. He saw him walk towards the fountain of the icy waters at the entrance to the village. In the pool of water Prefti Vlasë built dikes and filled them with the water overflowing from the basin. He had brought many a paper sailboat, which he sailed with the wind he himself provided by blowing puffs of air.

To the people of Sheshi, Prefti Vlasë was a disgrace. They blamed the Church officials in that faraway city for not rectifying the abomination. "Our children will never get to Paradise unless they are baptized," the women fussed as they sat outside the door of their homes knitting and mending. As they watched the nuns lock the door to the church with heavy bolts from the outside and the inside, the women resolved to bring their children into a state of grace and an understanding of the old ways.

The elders who lived at the end of the village near the church carved in the rock kept busy making cloth dolls for the newborn. As soon as they could stand on their feet and search the sky with their own eyes, the little ones were given a doll and were taken to the hill above the train station. There stood a round, grassy place, greener than any other in the lands pertaining to the village. The ancient grove was surrounded by uniformly tall cypress trees, and through it ran a spring of cold, clear water, sweeter than that of any other fountain. Called the "Fountain of Shea," it was sheltered and protected just as vigilantly as the Church of the Virgin of Constantinople on the hill overlooking Sheshi from the side of the nascent sun. There on a feast day just before sunset the young and the old, dressed in their best attire, would go to wash their hands and faces, to slice the watermelon which had been cooled in the waters, and to gather around the storyteller to listen to the tales of the days of old.

But, with the arrival of Prefti Vlasë in the village, the Fountain of Shea was kept hidden in the deepest memories of the people. No one dared go near it nor mention it by name. The mothers of Sheshi wanted their children to one day enter the "Gates of Paradise," so often mentioned by Prefti Vlasë as he stood tall on the pulpit of the Church of the Dead. They did not know exactly where nor how their children would enter these gates, but they wanted to make certain that they would not be excluded from them when they were no longer around to look after them.

The women of Sheshi never shared these concerns with their men. They only talked about them among themselves when the men were in the fields tending to the crops. The division of labor between the man and the woman was strict and abiding. In the home, the woman ruled like a queen bee, while growing certain crops and tending to them was a man's duty. Sickly as he was, Zelmi was caught, as he was growing up, between the secretive world of his mother (whom he followed daily in her house chores and during her many chats with other mothers of the village) and the silent, stern behavior of his father, who demanded complete obedience. So it was that a particular moment which occurred during the spring festivities at the Fountain of Shea often came to his mind.

Chapter Three

Zelmi's mother had spent the long winter months knitting the sweater and socks that he was to wear during the feast celebrating the end of his childhood. On the morning of the event, Zelmi's mother took her best common pin and placed it on the heart of the white woolen doll she had made for him. She put the doll inside a chestnut box and handed it to Zelmi. "When you reach the top of the hill beyond the railroad tracks," she told him, "look for the circular green space. You are first to wash your hands and feet and dry them with this white cloth. Place the doll under the volcanic rock and jump over it seven times. With your eyes closed, find the common pin on the doll and push it all the way inside the heart. Be certain not to open your eyes until you can hear the fluttering wings of the butterflies. You must bury the doll, wrapped within the white cloth, face down inside the green round space and then retrace your very same steps returning home. Do not look back, son, until you have reached the door to our house."

This was the day that changed Zelmi's life. Having finished the rite, he could feel the heaviness of his shoes as he descended the hill, but he resisted the temptation to look back at the white butterflies singing ancient lullabies. A cold sweat began to fall from his forehead, casting a shade over his eyes. The surroundings, so familiar to him the day before, suddenly seemed altogether strange. Zelmi no longer felt part of the trees gently swaying their multicolored leaves in the wind. Nor were the sounds and the smell of the wheat fields recognizable any more. For the first time, Zelmi became aware of strange cries reaching his ears from the deep precipices at the end of the village. Around him he saw the white butterflies bitten by armies of black flies pursuing them inside the prickly desert flowers that grew under the shade of the pine trees. His knees almost gave out, and the pain from his legs moved up to his throat, drying his mouth. A bitter, prickly sensation had replaced the sweetness of the waters from the Fountain of Shea.

Zelmi's mother, her eyes frightened and deeply recessed within their sockets, waited patiently for Zelmi outside the door of their single-room home. Her heart had ached with a thousand needles during the never-ending wait on that hot spring afternoon. She knew that soon she would no longer be able to claim her son as her own. From then on, he would have to follow the footsteps of his father and learn the workings of the soil, the ways of tending seeds, and the process of harvesting in the late days of summer and autumn.

Zelmi knew everyone in the village. The days for him would come and go with the heat of the bygone spring and the winds of fall. He now spent the heavy snowfalls of winter planning his trip up North. For Zelmi's mother, time was spent waiting for the letter from her husband. She had become the anchor of the family after her husband had decided to seek his fortune across the ocean. He was following his older sister, who had been sent to America to work as a seamstress.

"Be close to your mother," his father had admonished Zelmi. The young man stored those words deep in the recesses of his mind. When sitting alone in the empty square of Sheshi and before closing his eyes at night, he would repeat the words so as not to ever forget them. That responsibility grew heavier and heavier as years went by and his mother grew more and more dependent on him. He felt ashamed to go down to the narrow brook below the white cliff to play with the fish coming up for air from their summer hideouts.

The rainy season that followed seemed especially long to Zelmi. The village streets, cold and wet from the incessant rain, kept everyone indoors, yet leaving the house from time to time was the only way he could relieve his anguish about having to provide for his family in his father's absence. "He had no right," Zelmi would say to himself as he grew older, "to leave me in charge of the family." All the same, there were times that he missed his father so much that he felt his loss as a heavy pain which would lodge in his chest for days. Zelmi understood his father's desire to undertake the perilous voyage across the dark ocean, for he too now fought against time, which nestled year after year inside the clock, rendering everything so monotonous that it seemed to rob even the air that one needed to breathe.

And still the days dragged on. The people in the café waited patiently for the rains to break. His mother had lost count of the days that she had been waiting for the letter to arrive from that faraway place. "The city must be asleep, lulled by the bewitching sounds of the waves," she consoled herself.

On the day of his fourteenth birthday, Zelmi climbed up to the train station, where he was to join the endless trail of people going north. For months he had made preparations for the journey to the North without mentioning a word to his mother because he knew that she would be against it. The absence of his father had taken years of strength away from her. Not having her son to depend upon would certainly close the door to her hope of keeping the family together.

Of late, Zelmi had noticed that his mother had stopped looking into his eyes. She had begun to withdraw into her own world. From time to time she rearranged the few clothes she had saved for her daughter since her younger years. In the afternoon she sat next to the balcony, hoping to relive a bygone image of her husband returning from the fields. "How long before the clock strikes five o'clock?" she asked her neighbor, who daily came to have a cup of hot tea with her. The waiting lasted until the sun dropped behind the smallest of the seven mountains. "There is still plenty of time before five o'clock," her youngest son, Lini, would say, hoping to lessen her pain, so that she could close her eyes for the night. For it was the fading light of dusk which allowed the woman to shut her eyes; she opened them with the first light of dawn, when she resumed waiting for Dhimiter with the same precision, the same expectations.

Months before she had sensed the restlessness of her son, and in moments of lucidity she knew that sooner or later she would not see Zelmi sitting at the fireplace with his eyes fixed on the burning olive log. It was only a matter of time before Zelmi would climb towards the train station to board the early morning train that would take him to the city of lights that played luminous games with the wooden poles along its many streets. His mother had attempted many a night to imagine this terrible place that had lured her husband and now enticed her eldest son away from her home. It was a force that all her magic was unable to identify, but she could feel its monstrous strength snatching her family from her. The few times Zelmi dared to look at her as they sat next to the hearth, she cautioned, "If you want to leave, it is best that you not tell your younger brother. He might want to follow you, and he is not fully grown." She saw her family burning away like the few twigs in the fireplace used to start the burning of the olive stump. She fought the desire to curl up forever under the covers by thinking of the ashes she must save to give life to the dormant seeds of her garden.

And so it happened, to the surprise of no one, especially

not his mother, that one fine morning before dawn Zelmi kissed her and his younger sibling and climbed the hill to the train station without looking back. It was then that the bells of the clock tower in the square pierced his chest, freeing him of the pain that he had carried with him since that late afternoon when his father had left to cross the ocean. Little did he know, as he found the only seat available in the carriage that had stopped in front of him, that it would be the last time he would ever look upon his mother's face. Nor could he know that he would be unable to accompany his younger brother to his final resting place beyond the little church carved on the rock.

A few hours later his mother, having fallen asleep after dawn, awoke to a morning enveloped by a thick fog. The air weighed heavily on the few leaves left hanging on the almond trees by the wind of the previous night. She had difficulty starting the fire with the few twigs which she had brought from the pile of wood stashed outside. A cup of hot tea would give her the strength to put order to the house. She intended to dust the two pieces of furniture left to her by her great-aunt and to get rid of the spider webs that had multiplied in the four corners of the room. The tiny window that connected the house with the outside usually brought in just enough light to ensure visibility, but that morning it shone ever so brightly, revealing a great mass of steam filled with specks of dust hovering over the commode and the wide table.

With measured gestures, she filled her cup with hot water. The sugar bowl on top of the fireplace mantle was empty, but the few figs hanging on the string next to the entrance served to sweeten a bit the tea leaves. They were a good substitute for the costly granular sugar. It was a cold morning. The white vapor from the cup could be seen searching for the top of the room, taller than usual.

Then, motionless, she took her customary seat on the chair placed at the side of the window. This was her way to avoid forgetting the faces of the villagers passing by during their daily errands. For the first time she had to struggle to recognize the passersby. She became convinced that the village itself had grown old. The girls had streaks of white in their hair and wore suits designed for the men. But what unnerved her the most was seeing them walking by themselves, wrapped by a shawl of loneliness. It was the same feeling of emptiness that she had carried inside her womb for many years.

Now she relived Zelmi's departure, and her eyes filled with tears. She felt that the outside world was escaping her. She attempted to lift her arm to motion to the unrecognizable faces passing by every now and then, but she could find neither the energy nor the will to do so. Even the memories deep inside her mind, generally so helpful to her during the long, rainy afternoons in the past, could not be held together by the rings of time. No longer able to remember what day it was, she felt tossed in the air by the wind coming down from the mountains.

It was her younger son's voice behind her that brought her back to her chair. "Zelmi left you a note," he told her. He had not read it and it did not occur to him to think that his brother might have left. To him this was just another day doomed to pass like all the others with no change.

Lini had always been seen by the family as the young child fixed forever in that imaginary age that for many stood motionless. They did not realize that an inner boredom and an acute feeling of nausea was about to take possession of his mind. It had started years before during his first day of school as he took his place in the back of the makeshift classroom. The school was at the old widow's house at the other end of the village. Dhimiter never had made anything of his son's desire for isolation, nor had he been particularly concerned by Lini's obsessive search for all kinds of seeds to plant, which he collected from every street of the village. "It is child's play," Dhimiter would say when his wife inquired why he would not play with the neighborhood children. "Let him find his own way out of it. It is part of growing up."

The mother, however, felt a terrible premonition. Night after night she would experience dreadful dreams that served to increase her fright. She dreamed of her son falling down into a deep ravine as they were going to her father's fields next to the meandering brook to look for any ripe tomatoes to take home. She believed in the dream, yet she did not have the courage to share it with her husband. But when she was with her son, she glued her hand to his, wishing that he might never let go. At times, she wished she could lock her fingers with his and draw him back into her womb.

Lini missed his father. His mere presence would have filled him with strength and a willingness to go to school and to do well there. He remembered his father's eyes beaming with satisfaction in seeing him reading and interpreting passages from the New Testament. Too young to undertake a conversation with his father, Lini could not understand that Dhimiter had left to cross the ocean mostly thinking of a better and more secure future for his children.

The boys' mother would have been happy with the little they had as long as they could keep the family together. For her, it was useless to attempt to change one's destiny and face the forces outside one's own village. After all, she thought, they were placed in the village for a definite reason, and one should not deviate from it. She had come to realize all that in her own house as a young girl, but her husband would not abide by that belief. "If we were to follow our feeling, we would all end up eating hay," he admonished his wife every time she advised him not to fall prey to empty dreams. There was no way she could dissuade Dhimiter from leaving Sheshi and going to meet the eldest of his sisters in the lands beyond the vast ocean.

Not too long after Zelmi's departure, and while my mother was making preparations for our departure, Sheshi awoke to an intense heat wave that solidified the air and scorched the bark of every tree. The flowers turned brown and burned as they fell to the ground. By late afternoon, the village's streets lay beneath two inches of ashes still emitting a foul odor. The people of Sheshi, blinded by the inflammation of their tear glands, could no longer distinguish the houses. The trees that surrounded the village were left bare and deeply scarred. Lini felt a deep urge to retrace his steps over the carpet of ashes. He managed to reach the hazelnut grove, which still had a few leaves, on top of the ravine at the end of the village. He climbed the tallest of the trees, leaving behind imprints on the trunk. Days after the fruitless search for him, the villagers recalled seeing a boy sailing on a gray sailboat, a boy who turned into a bluebird in the early rays of the morning and flew daily towards the sun at exactly midday.

Once again, strange looking people came from far away places to kneel before the tree that never completely lost its leaves and which, on the anniversary of the fallen ashes, bloomed with white-orange flowers in the shape of tiny sailboats. The mother never witnessed this miracle. She did see her son Lini in her dreams at the bottom of the cliff, weaving sailboats with the blue grass growing along the hidden brook of the dark waters and blowing them upward over the branches of the hazelnut trees. Alexsa preserved in the deepest recesses of her memories the sound of the dark cool water bubbling out of the small crevices and making its way toward the cave of the serpent.

In her youth, Alexsa had heard many a version of the origin of the sacred cave which had the power to change anyone into the shape most desired. She specifically recalled that one winter night as she sat next to the fireplace crocheting the pillow cases of her future matrimonial bed, she had flown with the blue butterflies that had suddenly appeared on the white threads. But only after the disappearance of her younger son did those memories begin to make sense to her. Alexsa had found peace realizing how nothing dies, how everything that walks in the distance simply changes into something else to escape the smothering effects of time. She began to search in earnest for the past by invoking the spirits of her ancestors who had been waiting to receive her into the world of never-ending floating images.

Mitrusha, the widow who lived close to Alexsa, found her with wide open eyes and a soft smile at six that evening. Mitrusha had wanted to tell Alexsa of having seen her son Zelmi on the train that was moving towards the yellow plains. The sighting was also confirmed days later by a group of workers going to the tomato fields. The unusual uneasiness that assailed Mitrusha on that day compelled her to knock at the door of her neighbor and even to call Alexsa for the first time by her first name. Alexsa had had no time to share with Mitrusha the dream in which she had seen Lini descend into the ravine next to the sacred cave of the serpent. On that day Alexsa had waited for hours for Lini to return. He had gone down to the brook to catch frogs as they came out of the water attempting to snatch from the moon its first rays of light. "I only saw Zelmi this morning at a passenger window of the train," Mitrusha told Alexsa just before she turned pale. "I recognized him by his sad look," she continued as Alexsa turned completely white with deep patches of grey on her cheeks.

Alexsa was buried quickly in her family's tomb, which bore only her name. Years later, no one in the village could remember Alexsa, and no documentation was ever found in the town's municipal building that could attest to her having existed. The many birth and death certificates had crumbled to dust years before as the oldest of the clerks dared to stare at them.

On the day of his departure from Sheshi, Zelmi was totally distracted by his dream of striking it rich in the city of the North, so he did not sense the imminent closing of his one-room house as he waited for the train on the station platform. He stayed in a lone corner of the edifice to avoid being recognized by any other traveler from the village. Zelmi boarded the train at precisely five o'clock in the morning. The train had just a few carriages. The platform was completely empty. He could have sworn that the train had no beginning and no end. He moved quickly from one carriage to another looking for an empty seat. Zelmi had never seen so many different faces before, nor had he heard so many strange combinations of sounds from what he thought was the same language.

Zelmi found a seat in the corridor next to a closed window. Next to him was seated a dark woman with bright green eyes and curly black hair held back by a black scarf. Zelmi likened her to the roaming Gypsies he had seen in the village during the weekly market day. She had her eyes fixed upon the sea, which followed the swiftly moving train as it turned and swirled much as a snake under thick bushes. The stranger's solemn look brought to mind his mother's image. "She will understand why I had to leave," Zelmi murmured to himself while following the crashing of the sea waves against the rocky shoreline. How odd and callous did the long corridor of the train wagon seem, filled as it was with strangers glazed in by the silence of early dawn.

Zelmi wondered if the woman's intense green eyes were a reflection of internal images woven with screams of desperation. His mind rushed uncontrollably through every alley of Sheshi following the smell of the burning olive logs and ending at the front steps of the barber shop. He had not had time to say good bye to Viti, with whom he had spent many an afternoon in silence and who had been more than a friend to him. Viti had known all along that it was only a matter of time before the village would lose another young man. It was the curse that had settled in the village when the ancient memories had begun to fade.

"Go and see for yourself what is there on the other side of the seven mountains. It is the only way to be at peace with yourself. I know you will return as all of us did with our backs full of memories," Viti had told Zelmi the day he saw a deep emptiness in the younger man's eyes.

Now Zelmi shivered with the early frost of the morning as he looked through the compartment's window at the branches of the trees along the tracks bent by the weight of the dew iced during the cold night. It was a gray morning with deep crevices of silence. Zelmi shared the pain in the hearts of everyone on that minute train moving ever so fast towards the "promised land." It was a journey filled with tears and suffocated cries across an endless plain. "The journey will never end," Viti had told him. "It is part of us all. The sad thing is that we become aware of it when it is too late to tell our children. And so, the circle becomes wider and wider and the pain ever deeper."

The train ride towards the North seemed endless. Zelmi

took out the piece of bread and the hard cheese he had put aside the night before leaving the village. The first rays of the sun had just reached the window panes from the distant sea, revealing the tired passengers stretched in so many different ways in the crowded compartment. He wondered if they knew where they were going as his own mind kept going back to his house, searching frantically for his mother and brother.

He was torn between the need to find a road he could traverse alone and the trust placed on his shoulders by his father. "I shall write to them the minute I find my cousin. They knew I had to leave. I shall send them all my wages, and my mother will be the envy of everyone in the village." Yet, Zelmi could barely convince himself of his wishes. The hours on the train were making a nest deep inside his gut. For relief, he brought back to mind Mitrusha's words to his mother. "Zelmi will be the shoulders that will sustain you as your husband gathers the waves from the ocean." Zelmi's mother never paid too much attention to Mitrusha. She could never penetrate the thick veil that covered the old woman's face when she came down the steps and sat on the front stairs of their home. Indeed, Alexsa was the only one who noticed the invisible shroud on Mitrusha, but she had never made anything of it. She had thought that it was a trick of the sun shining on her forehead.

It was his second day on the train. The bare mountains and dry land of the South gave way to flatlands densely cultivated with fruit trees. In the evening Zelmi saw a wide river flowing rapidly among poplar trees. He even saw boats in the shape of houses with chimneys plying the river freely. This land was certainly different and densely green. "It must be very easy to grow all kinds of things with so much water all around it and the sky filled with rainy clouds," he speculated.

The train had picked up speed and was sailing effortlessly through the flat plain. Zelmi, observing the wrinkles in the sunburned faces of the passengers, aged by centuries of sadness and solitude, struggled to recall the smell of soft air that came to Sheshi from the sea in the early hours of the morning. The travelers spoke with their eyes and uttered no sound. The young and the old huddled against each other much as the people in Sheshi did during the long winter days. Zelmi could not help but discern how similar the children were to their parents. It was like looking into a mirror where much of the same combinations were pitted in the cycle of time. There was a bond between the past and the future that could not easily be broken, for each drew sustenance from it.

Zelmi was beginning to make sense of much of what his father had told him at the train station. "Keep the family together while I am gone. I shall return as soon as I have saved enough to buy some land to put an addition to our home." The feeling that his mother and younger sibling needed him made Zelmi extremely uneasy.

The train had come to a stop at a long station where many people were waiting to board. Others dressed in white uniforms pushed carts filled with sandwiches and bottles of water. They urged everyone to buy, for it was the last stop before the final outpost six hours away. Of the people inside the compartment, no one paid any attention to the call. Like Zelmi, they had counted their money and could not afford such amenities. Indeed, it had taken years for Zelmi to save enough money for the trip, and, had it not been for Viti's giving him the money he had originally set aside for a gift for his wife, Zelmi would never have been able to undertake the journey. Zelmi dared not look at anyone; nor had anyone in the compartment uttered a word to him. The world outside of Sheshi was as impenetrable as the people and the landscape he was seeing. All that the passengers shared was their fear of the unknown and the certainty of poverty and want. Among them there was a deep mistrust as dark as the deepest caves underneath the seven mountains. Behind their remote faces, there was a tightly restrained anger...a spark as yet incapable of igniting the fire which could only bring down the edifice that created the monster devouring all their efforts to provide for their families.

A feeling of malaise took hold of Zelmi's body. Nauseous from the bouncing of the carriages upon the tracks, he wished to leave the compartment and breathe a little of the air that was coming in from the opposite window of the long corridor. But the throngs of people sitting on the floor and on their own suitcases forced him to stay put. Placing his head against the window, he tried to close his eyes and ignore the queasiness aggravated by the sensation of closeness. He gasped for air as his eyes followed the clouds racing with the train.

Quite suddenly Zelmi felt the tip of a long sharp knife cutting through his abdomen. He recalled having felt the same pain when the train carrying his father away from the station at Sheshi had entered the dark tunnel. That pain would only subside when Zelmi sat on the steps of the Church of the Dead on hot summer days. Here Zelmi had no way of linking the pain he was feeling with what was about to happen, for he had never been able to foretell things the way his mother could. But it was exactly at the moment when Zelmi's pain grew most intense on the train speeding undetainably towards the northern white-capped mountains that Alexsa had given up the struggle to recognize the people that every now and then passed below the balcony of her home. Months later, as he still searched for a place familiar to him in the big city of the North, Zelmi was to become acutely aware of what had happened to his mother on that distant afternoon.

The train had increased its speed. "Are you comfortable?" the father asked the little girl who had been sleeping with her curly blonde head against his chest. There was no reply. Zelmi felt a compulsion to hear the sound of her voice and to touch her smile, a soft red petal bathed in early morning dew. She seemed terribly alone, close to and at the same time inexorably detached from her father. Zelmi thought of his younger brother, Lini, always standing close to his mother and tightly clinging to her skirt. Incapable of preventing it, Zelmi's eyes blurred. He found himself on his way back to Sheshi from his grandfather's olive grove. A line of women, dressed in black and bearing baskets of figs and white grapes, filed along the side of the road.

The sharp whistle of the locomotive entering the tunnel wrenched Zelmi's attention back to the sleepless girl across from his seat. A feeling of uneasiness had rooted in him. Why had he not been able to find work in the village? He did not need much. "A person can get by with very little," Viti had assured him repeatedly at the end of each conversation at the barber shop. "But you must first satisfy the thirst inside of you that searches for the vast spaces beyond the village." At times, Viti's words had made little sense, but Zelmi had known enough to grasp their seriousness even if he had not understood their full import. Many a time the words had put him on pins and needles as he sought to return home.

The pain in his stomach had extended to his knees, and still the little girl had not averted her eyes from his. The click-clacking of the wheels over the tracks was the only noise that penetrated the thick silence that had settled over everyone in the compartment. In the silence of this airless world, Zelmi heard someone standing outside in the corridor attempt a conversation. "I imagine the heat will let go by tomorrow." No response.

"Do they know where they are going? Will someone be waiting for them?" The fear that his cousin would not be at the station filled Zelmi with terrible apprehension. Zelmi felt as if he were being drawn down into a deep abyss with a huge serpent twisting into endless circles around a deep pool of cold waters with floating white flowers. Fish of all colors swam rapidly from one end to the other. From the mouth of the serpent an array of white lilies blanketed the water's surface.

"Tickets, please," announced the conductor with a stern but firm voice. Zelmi took out the ticket he had secured to his back pocket with a safety pin. The conductor took the ticket and verified the place of purchase and the final destination, written in bold black letters: Foggia-Milano. Zelmi noticed the sign of a serpent on the conductor's visor as he bent down to place the punched ticket in Zelmi's hand.

Morning had sneaked into the compartment unnoticed. Streaks of bright yellow light, awakening some and putting others further to sleep, were filtering through the shades of the small window. "In two hours we shall reach our stop," the little girl's father whispered softly to his wife, making every effort not to be heard by the line of people standing in the corridor. Zelmi wondered if that would also be his stop. The brightness of the sun and the deep green vegetation that followed the train invigorated his trembling body. He had kept vividly in mind the description of the train station given to him by his cousin as they had sat on the steps of the Church of the Dead in Sheshi. "In that land, the white clouds float over gentle winds, always searching to anchor themselves over the pinnacles of the snowy mountains."

In spite of having exchanged not a word with them, Zelmi felt a sense of serenity and warmth simply by watching the family with whom he had shared the journey. Now the announcement by the conductor, who moved from carriage to carriage indicating their imminent arrival at the central station, moved the people to organize their suitcases for quick claim. "Ilía, stay close to me and hold on to my skirt," the mother admonished the little girl as they stood in line to get off the train. Zelmi followed the family through the wide corridor of the train station, filled with throngs of passengers. The crowd moved quickly, almost to the rhythm of the departing train. Years later, while holding on to his cane and waiting for the black swallows to begin their late afternoon chase of the sound of the bell on top of the church belfry, Zelmi was to relive daily that little girl's pristine smile fading away in the distance. His eyes would fill with tears, which he gently wiped with the back of his hand while pretending to sweep away some dust from them. He could no longer keep alive the memories of the big city.

A cold night greeted Zelmi as he found his way out of the train station. The steep staircase down to the main street of the railroad building drowned him in the vortex of an asphyxiating silence. The air was filled with minute frozen icicles. At the end of the street, the last passengers had turned the corner, leaving the train station with a carpet of desolation. It was unbearably cold. Zelmi searched frantically for his cousin's address.

He returned to the waiting room at the bottom of the stairs and found an empty space in the far corner. The place was filled with people, their bodies motionless, their expressions lost. As some figures lay stretched upon the wooden benches, an old woman made a desperate search for something inside a brown canvas bag. Near her, a young man with a thick, unkempt black beard pressed his knees together as he rocked his head continuously from side to side. Yet no one seemed to notice anyone else or to be bothered by the strange aspect that each displayed. Zelmi soon convinced himself that they all suffered from the sickness of the loss of time. The four big clocks placed equidistantly around the perimeter of the circular hall were further proof to him that that was indeed the case.

Zelmi sat motionless in the only empty space in the place. His stomach began to convulse, and he had to struggle to hold back the pernicious feeling of nausea that had accompanied him throughout the journey. "If only I could make some sense of this world of grey clouds and interminable rains which keep people inside their places like mushrooms clinging to the bark of a tree." Abruptly, Zelmi realized the danger of talking to himself. He remembered the advice the priest in Sheshi had given him in the confessional booth when he had spoken of the deceptions in his mind. "Do not forget to leave behind a trail of stones that will guide you back from the maze of the mind. Always build bridges with every stone that you can find."

It was early in the morning and the sun had not yet broken through the clouds. Now the waiting room smelled of smoke and unwashed clothes. Upon opening his eyes, Zelmi noticed that no one had moved from the places they had occupied the night before. Still clutching his suitcase, Zelmi sought a place where he could wash his face. "Why was it that no one in the waiting room noticed my presence? Did they not know that I was one of them?" Now the nausea which had traveled with him took complete possession of his body. What remained under his control was his desire to climb over the wall of the train station to the unfamiliar world outside in spite of the fact that his legs felt like two logs with roots still attached to the earth.

Zelmi was the only one on the wide platform with the trains arriving and departing who seemed aware of his surroundings. In the only coffee shop in the station, the people in a row at the counter appeared to rotate endlessly on round stools, their uniform positions contrasting sharply with the mobility of their seats, which looked suspended in mid-air. Here the dank air, smelling of wet, decayed wood, found its way into Zelmi's lungs. The distance was still lost in utter darkness.

Along the platform, a semi-lit sign pointed to an abandoned waiting room where the crazed paint had turned the walls into multicolored spider webs. A sound of dripping water from the sink broke the deep well of silence which inhabited the place. Making his way back to the hall where he had spent the night, Zelmi sat with his legs crossed next to the charcoal-burning stove. He made an effort to recall the smile of the little girl as she had waved good-bye, but she had faded into the deep recesses of his mind as distant as the emptiness that reigned in the waiting room. It was then that Zelmi understood the implacable separateness and the inevitable distance that follows as one image stumbles upon another. Viti had often spoken to him about the feeling of emptiness that afflicted those who had gone north. "I do not know how to describe it to you," he had said. "You must come face to face with it to feel the file scraping over the surface of your bones. It opens deep cavities in everything that you see and gives you no time to gather back the broken fragments."

Zelmi did not even have the strength to lift his eyes to see if any sunlight from outside had made it into the waiting room through the round upper window. He closed his eyes and wrapped his hands around his waist. The fenced-in bodies surrounding him were no more than inanimate objects to be discarded.

Hours, perhaps days had gone by when Zelmi was awakened with a gentle kick on his shoes by a young man in uniform. Dazed and bewildered, Zelmi opened his eyes but remained speechless. "It is forbidden to sit on the floor. Either find a seat, if there is one available, or move out of the station," the guard murmured with a faint smile. He had seen so many like Zelmi that he had come to think of them as unwanted objects floating ashore. His eyes met Zelmi's for a fleeting moment. It was just long enough for the guard to reach into his pocket and take out a card with the address of a church which had set aside space to receive and give aid to the many stranded people in the big station. "Here," he said to Zelmi. "The church is only a few blocks from the station. Turn right as you leave, and look for the bell tower with a bronze cross on top."

Zelmi still hoped that his cousin would soon come to the station to look for him so he did not move. "Egidio will come before it gets dark," he comforted himself. But hours went by and the traffic at the station lessened. Most of the shops facing the tracks had turned off their lights as the day drew to an end like so many others. With hesitation, Zelmi forced himself to stand. He took the address which the guard with the smile of a newborn child had given to him.

The rain had turned into a soft drizzle which settled on his clothes as dew on flowers on an early summer morning. The street was caped in silence. The long road ahead of Zelmi seemed as inaccessible as the horizon beyond the seven mountains. The fog that had settled surreptitiously over the roof tops prevented him from seeing the bell tower, but Zelmi could make out a church with a lonely light at its front entrance. "Perhaps," he thought, "Egidio will be coming tomorrow to get me." The church door had been left ajar. He saw an empty corridor with one room lit at the end and proceeded with a heavy heart toward it. At a wooden table in the middle of the room people were eating bowls of soup with bits of bread in it. No one had noticed his entrance.

Zelmi sat on the bench that stood outside the door and waited for someone to come and claim him. He looked around, sensing that a world of darkness was laying siege. He looked for support but could find nothing to hold onto. Suddenly a vision appeared in the distance. It was that of a woman with dark streaks running down her face. Her eyes were wide open, frightened and bulging as if wanting to hold onto something Zelmi could not see. "Why didn't they close her eyes?" Zelmi had no way of knowing that the neighbors did try to no avail to close his mother's eyes after they removed her from the chair near the balcony; her eyelids were as stiff as her fingers. No one that night dared to look at Alexa's eyes, which seemed to suck everything inside them like a hungry whirlwind. They had to place a heavy glass over the casket to prevent the household objects from falling into the swirling tunnel. The magnetic force of the eyes emptied the house of most of its belongings. Even the door of the house was loosening from its hinges. The mayor of the town, who was known for his quick decisions, ordered the keeper of the cemetery to immediately bury the body fifty feet deep and to place upon it boulders rolled down over freshly cut tree trunks from the tallest of the seven mountains. The whole town was mobilized to deal with the situation that threatened to swallow everything they possessed. Zelmi prayed for the skin to soften over his mother's eyes. The piercing rays emanating from Alexa's eyes had traveled for three days and two nights searching to bring Zelmi back to her. "I must close them. She must find peace," he muttered as another voice was making its way to him. The comforting welcome of the priest of that house of succor lessened his anxiety.

Zelmi opened his eyes and halfway met those of the priest in charge of the home. The priest's face and understanding expression reminded him of Viti. He felt Viti's strength as the priest helped him rise from the bench. "There is a seat on the other side of the table," he said. "I will bring you a bowl of soup with a slice of bread." Zelmi moved slowly and certainly as he looked for the empty space at the end of the long wooden table. No one of the innumerable people looked up to see who this new arrival was. For a time, only the sound of the silverware broke the silence enveloping the room. Each of them, and Zelmi had counted them one by one, appeared to be adrift. They were of all ages, totally detached from the rhythm of the seasons. They had become diseased and no one dared to cure them. Zelmi realized that he had entered a place of last refuge, where solace substituted for any direct intervention to cure the sickness. He remained frozen, overwhelmed by what he was seeing. The person ("I wish I knew his name.") sitting next to Zelmi snatched away the piece of bread that the priest had given him. Zelmi made no attempt to stop him. "I would have given him the bowl of soup had he given me any indication that he wanted it." The fellow was much younger than Zelmi, who came to see in him the attempt to disguise the fear in his eyes as mere hunger. Zelmi wondered if he, too, had lost the way to return home.

"I am waiting for my cousin to come to get me; I shall not remain here much longer," Zelmi hastened to say. He dared not look directly at the person next to him.

"No one comes here." The comment came quickly from

someone else at the end of the table. "They will no longer provide me with paper and pencil to keep count of the days," the same person complained. The conviction with which those words were spoken startled Zelmi. They had come from someone who lived life inside a plastic case.

"We all have been waiting for a long time for someone to call on us," the one sitting next to Zelmi whispered softly. "Do you still want the bowl of soup?"

A prolonged silence followed. Zelmi tried to control the involuntary twisting of his fingers. He felt his blood receding to a hidden place in his body, turning him into a figure much like the rest. The confusion in Zelmi's mind and his inability to find a way out of the situation and into the horizon of his memories convinced him that he indeed had become part of the group sitting rigidly around the long table. The door to the dining hall had been closed and a visible silence hung over the table.

"This winter the fog descending from the seven mountains will loom over Sheshi for months. They should place warning signs on the road beyond the train station. I should have told mother of my decision to go north. Viti promised me that he would tell her of my intentions only after my departure. Viti was right about this part of the world. The wide illuminated streets are crammed with autos in every little space on each side, and the cobblestones multiply the gray colors, forging knots with the street lamps hanging from electric wires. There are so many closed doors. The windows are shut tight, and the plaster walls are lined up like the cypresses along the road to Sheshi's cemetery. On the walls there are many writings which I cannot decipher. You were right, Viti. The eyes of the city carve deep crevices inside a person. They twist into and probe the realm of loneliness that never leaves us."

"The door will be opened tomorrow at dawn. The priest will be bringing a bowl of warm coffee-milk with a slice of bread," someone uttered. The familiar sound brought Zelmi back from daydreaming. Sheshi vanished, taking with it the sweet scent of almond trees of early spring. Zelmi hesitated to answer the man, whose face he could not discern.

The music from a lone guitar filtered, note by note, through the window into the refectory. Zelmi could not see outside, for the shutters were closed and it was dark. The small light that hung from the ceiling swung like a leaf in late autumn.

"In a little while they will turn the light off," enunciated the same unseen person. "Do not take your hands out of your pockets. Many of us were stripped of all we had. They say it is the priest in the black robes who comes during the night, walking two feet above the ground and snatching our belongings. Some swear that his eyes turn fiery red, like a rod sensing where the money is. I myself had hidden mine in my sock inside the shoe under my pillow. I had made three knots in the sock to ward off the evil spirits. Yes, I had learned to do that from my grandmother, God bless her soul. She was a fine person. When I woke up in the morning, with the sun shining right on top of my eyes, I reached for the sock. The knots were all undone as if I had never made any, and the money was gone. I did not mention it to anyone; you are the first to hear of it. Not because I trust you completely, not yet, anyway, but because there is something in your eyes that wants to listen to me. Yes, the eyes tell everything. They say that the eyes can make and unmake a person. Well, I thought you should know what happens here during the night, for in just a little while the light that shines above us will be turned off. Can you sleep with one eye open as some people do?"

Zelmi could still not see his face. "In the morning I shall ask for his name. I cannot now. It is pitch dark and it is best that I stay awake. I cannot lose the little money that Viti saved for me. I wish I had never left the village. Had I listened to my mother, I would not find myself in this accursed place. The conversations at Viti's shoe store insisting that the future of the young could only be found by going north twisted my mind. I thought of nothing else but leaving Sheshi. 'Up north, there is work for anyone willing,' they would say. 'The people are orderly and there is running water inside the small rooms where the workers stay, and there are mirrors on top of the sinks so that a person can look as neat as the ones walking in the streets. No one up north bothers with useless conversations. It is true that they are mostly silent and never take their eyes from what they are doing. A young man cannot rot in this isolated village where time lies still.'"

Zelmi sat for hours on the lower hill of Sheshi watching the few automobiles that whisked over the asphalt road in the near distance. "I always thought that the drivers were looking for their way home. At times a driver would stop for a short while, change the tire and speed off again. No one of them ever came up to our village to see what it looked like. Perhaps they had no time. Or maybe they could not even see the houses because of the rays of the hot sun overhead. Sometimes you could not tell the difference between the light from the sun and the white-washed walls of the homes in the village. The houses seemed to be tied to the treeless mountain above it. Now in this dark place where I can only hear the fearful breathing of the others, I do miss the village."

Zelmi thought of his mother. "Don't go out of the house. The fields are full of vipers during the early afternoon."

Zelmi could feel the heat of the sun penetrating through his clothes and warming his skin. He smelled the recently cut hay and saw the swallows feeding on the seeds lifted by the wind in mid-air. The earth, garnished green and silver, was playing music with the chirping birds. They had gathered for a feeding frenzy in the almond trees.

"I think I am falling asleep," Zelmi whispered to himself. "I can barely hear the uneasy breathing of the one next to me. I cannot say how many hours have gone by, but dawn will be here soon. I think I can smell the dew falling gently from the passing clouds looking for a soft place to land."

Zelmi was determined to keep his eyes open until his cousin came to fetch him. "Someone will show him the way to this place of refuge," Zelmi assured himself. "It is right next to the train station. Perhaps the same guard with the sad eyes will show him the way. Yes, I told the guard that my cousin was to pick me up."

Zelmi could not recall fully what the guard had answered him, but he did recall the warnings. "Do not be in a hurry to leave the hospice. The people outside the train station walk up and down the street with measured steps. They won't recognize you if you walk too fast. You have to observe and memorize their rhythm, their facial expressions, and you have to know exactly when to smile at someone. Do not be in haste. You'll end up smiling at the wrong time, and that will be the signal for the people in the white uniforms to take you away in their blue trucks. They will dispose of you and no one will ever know anything about it. Not even your cousin. The trucks follow a side street with no lights; the buildings on that street have no doors."

Zelmi thought he heard the door knob to the refectory turning, but he could not remember the location of the door. He had not looked back when the priest had brought him into the room. He wanted to talk to the person next to him, to see his face before leaving. He pushed the slice of bread toward him, but the streak of light from the top window was too weak to reach the long table.

Zelmi spoke to himself without realizing it. "I never did get to look at his face. My shoes seemed to crush my feet. I wanted to untie them and place them over my shoulders. I recalled my grandfather with his shiny black shoes in the coffin in the middle of the house and the wooden stool that I climbed up on to take a better look at him. As I peeked through the glass cover over the wooden box I noticed that one of the shoelaces was untied. 'Mother, Grandfather does not want to leave yet; his shoe is untied.'

"'Quiet,' she whispered into my ear so that the other women wailing would not hear. 'He is not going away forever. One day each one of us will join him. It is only a matter of waiting for the right chance. Remember well and make certain that you do so,' she used to remind all of us, especially on rainy days when people do crazy things just to forget what awaits them at the end. As for me, I am not going to wait for anyone anymore. The men in the white uniforms will soon come to get me. I will be tied to a tree and left there to dry like bark. I hope they leave me where there is a flock of sheep grazing on the deep, green grass like that on each side of the winding brook below Sheshi. I remember Grandfather expressing the same wish on a clear summer afternoon. When I told Mother of his wish she said she wasn't sure she could satisfy it because she could not find the date on the calendar even after years and years of searching for it."

Zelmi did not dare to untie his other shoe for fear that his movements would awaken the others. Someone was moaning at the far end of the refectory. Zelmi could have sworn that the man next to him had dozed off, but he now heard him say, "Do not be concerned. It is fear. Fear of the dark. Fear that he will no longer have the will or the strength to wait for someone. I am certain that by daybreak he will feel much better. Just rest for now, but do not fall asleep. I'll talk to you in the morning."

"When everyone had left the room, Mother had hastened to remove the glass lid from the coffin. With tears in her eyes, she had tied the lace of the left shoe. 'I don't want your grandfather to wander from this life and through the other without being able to find the repose he is looking for.'"

The silence of the refectory was slowly receding as the streak of light in the upper window grew wider. Zelmi checked the money in his pocket, which he knew was sufficient to buy him a ticket back to Sheshi. His pocket was empty. Searching frantically all about him, he appealed in a choking voice to the priest who entered. The cleric tried to calm him.

"My son, this is the house of God. No one robs anyone here. God protects you all. You are his children. You must have spent the money."

"Where is the person who was in the spot right next to me?"

"No one has been there since the gypsy left a year ago today. If you need work, you should stand outside the house with the others. They are picked up for a day's work early in the morning. Don't stand back. Show them that you are eager. We won't be able to keep you here unless you are able to contribute to your needs."

Zelmi did not reply. The pain in his lower abdomen carved his insides like a knife gutting a pig. Zelmi felt just like the pig which might manage to escape the clutches of the men holding it down only to run about with a knife still dangling from its throat. The butchers would not even bother to chase it. "He can't go far. Later we will follow the trail of blood and bring him back."

If he could have done so, Zelmi would have screamed from the bottom of his guts to get rid of that knife scraping the flesh from his ribs. He did not know what to do. His trembling legs would not respond when he attempted to stand up and face the day. He had never been one to complain or ask for help. He moved towards the door. Even then, no one looked at him. The wall of silence that had kept him company during the never-ending night continued to engulf the others. Without having had the chance to get to know anyone, Zelmi opened the only door of the house of refuge and faced the cold, wintry morning of the northern city.

The sidewalks were lined with shivering men with their hands hidden inside their coats. They only lifted their lowered heads when they heard the noise of a vehicle passing by, hoping that it would stop right next to them and offer work for the day. Their sorry appearance reminded Zelmi of the flocks of sheep herded by growling black dogs straight down from the mountain pastures towards the slaughterhouse. Zelmi wanted to turn back, but he saw the priest closing the door behind him with a surreptitious smile.

"Now I am one of them, but I will not be sucked in by that man," he managed to murmur. So Zelmi took his place among the men and hoped that someone would stop to offer him work. "The one who leaves his place of birth knows what he leaves behind but he does not know what he is going to find." This had been Alexa's way of telling her son to clear his mind of false desires and dreams of other places.

Zelmi found himself alone among a throng of impenetrable bodies shivering under the constant icy drizzle that had begun to drench their heads. A woman of no more than twenty, with a shawl pulled over her hair and tied in front, yelled, calling her husband's attention as he stood with his eyes downcast: "The child needs some powdered milk." The miniscule man answered by nodding.

"You will always be with us at the barber shop, I promise you. Our conversations will never stop. They will keep you warm when you are not noticed by anyone in the streets." Zelmi found himself gasping for a deep breath.

"If no one stops for me, I shall go back to the waiting room in the train station." The street signs were rendered invisible by the rain drops. "I really do not know why Egidio hasn't come for me yet."

The lines of people waiting to be picked up had grown shorter. Many had given up, planning to come back the next day. The sky was filled with gray and black streaks. On the steps of a building sat an old man resting his chin on a wooden cane. Zelmi could see the wrinkles burrowing into his forehead. His lips were tightly sealed and his hat channeled the rain away from his eyes. A man and a woman on the opposite side of the street had joined hands and started to walk in silence toward a cluster of trees on top of the hill.

The penetrating dampness convinced Zelmi that he needed to get to the train station. The couple in the park had melted into the fog by now, and the light from the street lamps was turning the puddles into a silver chain. Following the barely visible signs toward the station, Zelmi sailed into the sea, thrust forward by the desire to find his cousin. "He must be waiting for me," he mumbled in a tattered voice as he avoided the broken bottles lying on the sidewalk. The garbage cans had been flipped over by the wind, and the stench from them was unbearable. Stray dogs searched for bits of leftovers in them or nosed through the debris which littered the ground. Zelmi was hoping to meet someone coming his way so that he might bid him "good day" just for the sound of a voice. "Maybe with some luck I could even brush my coat against theirs." By now the rain was pouring down in sheets.

"The harvest this year will be lost unless it rains for a day or two." Zelmi pivoted to see who had spoken. "The grapes need water." The priest had summoned the people to lead a procession to the old Church of the Virgin of Constantinople. "I shall be back after the Mass. Make sure your brother stays home with you. He had a bad night and his fever was high; I had to change his wet clothes three times to keep him cool."

Zelmi remembered the night clearly. "I kept him next to me as he trembled all over. I held his hand tightly and told him to think of the red poppies in the wheat field beyond the winding brook. 'When will Father come home?' he had pressed. 'He has been away many days and nights. Mother tells me that we still have to wait many more summers before he can save enough money to send for us. Do you miss Father?' I told him that I missed Father as much as he did, but I could not show any weakness to the people of Sheshi. It would not be manly. I remember to this day how he nodded his head without asking any more questions."

On his way to the station, Zelmi, feeling alone amidst so much silence, noted the windows with iron shutters that locked the people in. There was blackness on the walls and the air was putrid. In the distance, he saw the reflection of someone approaching as if carried by the fog; it was an old man, bent almost to the ground and holding a small dog on a leash. They walked slowly together, almost stopping simultaneously to gasp for air. The little dog turned up its face, looking at its owner as if waiting for a signal to take the next step.

Holding onto the iron gate at the entrance of the station, he realized how similar is the condition of all people who wait to gather the residue of time. The road from Sheshi to the fields seemed so far away. The earth with its open veins waited to be blessed with drops of wind and seeded before sunset. With hopes of a better harvest to come and with their backs bent, the peasants, followed by their dogs, climbed toward the village.

"I walked towards the old man and the dog, wondering if he would help me find my way back to the waiting room. The street was covered with a mantle of silence. I quickened my pace, nearing the miniscule figure who paused after each step. The raindrops searched frantically for the stream of water that would carry them to their resting place near the coal-burning stove in the corner of the waiting room. There I could talk to the old man without calling anyone's attention. I had to avoid being seen by the station guard. I would not again listen to that soft voice nor be beguiled by those innocent eyes.

"'I have been waiting for someone to notice me,' remarked the old man the moment I got close to him. I had the sense that he had been waiting for me for a long time. As for me, I felt something surging up from inside as I reached out to touch his hand. It was the coldness of the night. He lifted his eyes, blurred by a deep blue film lining the tunnel that led to his inner world. 'I have been walking this street with my companion for many years. I come out at night because I see better in the dark. Years ago, I made the mistake of getting off at the wrong train station. In fact, it was many, many years ago. I cannot tell exactly how many. This street seems to get longer and narrower with the passing of the seasons. At times I send my dog a few steps ahead to see if he recognizes someone from the past days, but his sight is not what it used to be, either. He relies mostly on scent.'"

The two figures on that cold, tunneled street...one bent over by the weight of wingless hopes and the other, slim and youthful...were not seen by anyone else that night. The old man had been given no indication; there had been no premonitions in his dreams that he was to leave his room for the last time in search of someone to recognize.

Zelmi was never to learn the name of the old man on the street facing the train station of the city of the north. As I sit with my eyes fully open in this compartment, next to my mother, I observe each of the passengers. The woman in front of us still holds her lips tightly and her forehead straight. I can see the dark circles under her eyes welding rings together, but I cannot see who is holding the end of the chain outside the train compartment. The speed with which the train moves into the heart of the night blinds me. I cannot see outside of the memories. Grandfather Zelmi was right when he warned me not to trust the reflection created by the shifting rays of the sun. "The mirror and light are there to trick you to come out of your cave. The mirror fragments your memories and light fades them. Keep alive the remembrances of the past. Those who came before need you to keep them alive. It will be your thoughts of them and your constant shaping and reliving of the past events that will be nourishing to you as you begin the struggle against the light and the mirror."

Chapter Four

Now that I find myself next to my mother going to the big city that plays with the waves of the sea, I recall clearly those dry, warm summer afternoons walking with Grandfather Zelmi towards the chestnut grove to check on the few squash seeds he had planted between the rows of trees. It would take us hours to get to the top of the hill where he owned that small grove given to him by his father. The village at that time was a large playground lined with almond trees, like the ones I used to see in the magazines at Prefti Vlasë's parish house after the hour of catechism class. In time, the narrow winding streets of Sheshi suddenly came to an end with others opening secretly on the left but most of the time on the right. It was like a maze to us as we ran hiding from one another until thirst summoned us to the main square where fountains provided the cold water that had slid down from deep within the seven mountains.

One afternoon, as we walked back from the field of the tall chestnut trees, I asked Mother if Grandfather Zelmi had eyes that looked inside people's minds. My mother scolded me, thinking that I was making fun of his condition. She told me never to speak that way in his presence. "We have to make his short stay with us as pleasant as we can and help him along as he retraces his steps before the final breath."

Grandfather Zelmi went on for long periods speaking vividly of timeless memories. "I could only imagine the pain one would feel if unable to breathe, and that was because many times, with friends, I attempted to hold my breath longer than they. I can still feel the pain now in the lower part of the stomach right next to the navel."

"Yes, I had been waiting for many years to learn the name of that old man with the dog. (I had been preparing myself to go there ever since the conversation in the barbershop.) At night, before closing my eyes, I would follow the road to the train station of Sheshi counting the steps and placing ribbons on each tree. I climbed that dusty road so many times that even now I can recall the number of rocks along it and the type of plants that grow on either side. The desire to leave Sheshi and to see the big city of the north had taken total possession of me. It soon became an obsession. I saw it everywhere, even drew tall buildings and the unending tracks of its train station on the fig leaves I would save and dry carefully under the hot sun. I pretended I had a cousin who had established himself there and was waiting for my arrival. It all seemed so real until I could no longer tell which the true one was: my cousin or I. The people of Sheshi were right. I let go of the rope everyone else was holding onto. My friends avoided me as if I carried a contagious disease. Many a door would close on me as I walked down the road towards the unending brook to watch the fish jump into the air, reaching for sunlight.

"From time to time Viti would give me an apple saved from the previous harvest. With the arrival of the first cold winds, I helped him find the wood for the winter. I would sit on his barber shop steps waiting for your great-grandmother to return from gathering the few tomatoes or one or two clusters of white grapes overlooked by the pickers in the fields beyond the brook.

"People, especially in the evening hours, would come to Sheshi's only barber shop for a quick shave. Very few had their hair cut; those who did were mostly young. They came in with a clean shirt and a jacket, leaving behind, as they moved on to the square, a scent that reminded me of the plants that grow very tall on top of the sacred cave. I could see the swarms of tiny, shiny mosquitoes following them, swirling through the air. They never did come close to me, however, for I would have chased them away.

"The time came when people noticed if the barber shop was open or not or if I would be there, seated on the same spot. Little did they know that the conversations I overheard would poison my imagination. I was drawn to those steps the minute the sun reached its zenith over the church belfry. The almond trees were in full bloom and the swallows swooped into the sky, diving every now and then, beak first, into the cold waters of the fountains.

"At this hour the barber shop in Sheshi became a hub of stories. Those who came in to make themselves presentable to the others in the main square of the village came also to be enchanted by the stories told and to enter the gates of fabled lands. It was an initiation that lasted all afternoon. The shattering of the old strictures nourished their childhood curiosity, kept hidden from others during their daily activities in the fields and during their encounters in the square in the late afternoons. At night, while sitting motionless outside the café entrance, they lived the unshared adventures in their own chosen spaces, traveling over long and perilous roads, slaying dragons, and rescuing young maidens just as the cinema heroes did in the first movies that had been shown in the village. Their minds would tell and retell those events, polishing and adding unseen elements which turned them into silent stories. Sheshi became a sea of stories with storytellers young and old. It must have been the warmth of the wood burning slowly in the fireplaces of the village and the countless sparks emanating from the logs that inspired them to tell of these legends.

"'During the annual festival of songs,' the storytellers would recount, 'in a city whose waters were as blue as the sky after sunset, sweet melodies rose from the depths of the sea.'

"The barber shop filled with people eagerly waiting, with fingers crossed, for Viti's magic hand to bring those sweet, torturing melodies from the city beyond everyone's reach. The small shop, with two large mirrors in front of two revolving chairs, was blanketed in deep silence. The sonorous wind coming from the ridges of the seven mountains filled the sky over the village with stimulating sounds, causing the swallows, inebriated by the strange harmony beating against their wings, to interrupt their flight in mid-air. The doors of the houses that had been shut for months during the cold days of winter now opened. The hinges and locks were drawn out of their places by the sweet sounds. It was the hour in which Sheshi would fall into the deepest recesses of dreams. No one would see or feel the presence of others. During the playing of songs, the young girls would hasten to select the best flowers from their vases and to save them in white envelopes with the hope of contracting the sound and their aroma into one single sensation. The houses smelled of spring and of sights of love which confounded even the eldest women in the village. The elders themselves could not decipher the phenomenon. It had never happened before. 'The world has certainly changed, and we were not even aware that those changes were coming,' they murmured softly to one another.

"They blamed it on the people, particularly on the young, who, during the summer months, disseminated strange ideas gotten from other lands and displayed unrecognizable items which confounded those of Sheshi to the point of forcing each of them to latch his door with the heaviest key. During the early afternoon hours, the Devil would roam freely through the village streets, handing out drawings of things and places that no one could identify.

"The only people who knew the source of the strange designs were those who had gone beyond the snow-capped mountains in search of their relatives to places where strange things happened. 'There,' they would say, 'people do not understand one another. Each one speaks his own language. Bright lights and unfamiliar, sweet sounds move people from one place to another.'

"But very few of those listening understood what was being said in the barber shop. The machine that produced the captivating sounds was the prime gift of the owner of the barber shop. He had received it from his cousin in a wooden box stamped all over with the word 'fragile' in bold letters. 'I can only tell you,' he would insist, 'that the machine came from the land where dreams and despair grow like fruit on trees.'

"Most of the people who listened to the explanation paid no attention to it. They were concerned neither with the origins of those songs nor with the channels through which they emerged; but they simply could not listen to them enough. Although listening made them feel strange, the songs also filled their inner spaces with a pleasant sensation of lightness. The experience reminded them of the vibrating flight of the mockingbirds over the pomegranate trees. Sooner than imaginable, the square in Sheshi became the place where everyone, young and old, would gather to try to whisper from memory the melodies heard outside the barber shop. The women, sitting on balconies screened by vases of basil and parsley, were convinced that it was a side effect of the burned oats their men drank with hot water at the café. 'If this continues,' said Serafina to the neighbor with whom she shared half the balcony, 'the men will forget how to work the land and we will all starve to death.'

"That very evening they decided to share their concerns

about the dangerous effect of the coffee on their men openly with the priest. It was the hour before the recitation of the novena. The women were not aware that the priest himself had fallen into the habit of having hot coffee four times a day, starting at eight in the morning. This precise ritual occurred on the hours he carefully marked on a calendar with a perfect circle over the twelve hours of the day and the twelve hours of the night. He kept both the calendar and the sacred book locked in the chestnut bookcase.

"'Having a cup of coffee with friends in the afternoon is a spiritual necessity,' the priest assured his concerned parishioners. Prefti Vlasë had been the parish priest for many years and so understood the need for a person to reminisce with a cup of hot coffee. It was his way of tapping the private inner realm.

"For the rest of the people, the town's small theatre, built on the outer road that led to the cemetery, offered them the same escapades. The town's authorities had decided that the theatre be built away from places frequented by the women of the village. Mothers and wives insisted that their sons and husbands not leave the theatre laden with dreams.

"The theatre soon became a window to the outside world. The screen was filled with all kinds of vast prairies where dozens of soldiers in dark blue uniforms chased Indians decorated with feathers and riding pinto ponies. Or again, there were ships with endless lights floating on seas as the waves washed their sides; below deck were ballrooms decorated with multicolored lights more varied than those of the firmament. Crammed within them were languid women with cheeks as white as goat's milk, bending and sighing to the sound of music played by so many different instruments. Accompanying these sylphs were men all attired in identical formal garments.

"Not long after the first opening, the movie house became a threat to the peace of mind of the people of Sheshi. On Sundays, standing taller than usual, Prefti Vlasë exhorted the women who attended Mass to keep their men at home even if they had to enchant them. 'The men of the village are not paying attention to the children, nor are they keeping their marital obligations,' the priest cried.

"Indeed, whether at home or in the fields, whether awake or asleep, the men could not keep their minds off those magical places or those beautiful, delicate butterfly faces seen on the silver screen. On Sunday afternoons, after the last showing, the whole crowd, falling into a deep stupor, was given over to dreams. It was as if everyone were in a daze. Even the women, mending old work clothes behind the window curtains or seated on the balconies, had difficulty recognizing their own men.

"But the 'disease,' as Prefti Vlasë called it for lack of a better word, ended up infecting him, as well. He would ask the young men (those few who had been forced by circumstances to attend Sunday Mass) to confess all that which they had seen at the movie house.

"'It is like no other thing ever witnessed or heard of before,' they would say. 'It makes one want to go to those places and to touch the people who live in them.'

"Another confessed, 'I get a terrible pain in my lower abdomen, and it only abates when I write about the swallows and the flowers that bloom in early spring down below the village along the winding brook.'

"Prefti Vlasë understood very well what was happening to the young men. 'They are coming of age sooner than they should,' he would murmur to himself. At times, during the celebration of the Mass, he would notice them gripping love letters, which they stealthily transferred to the trembling hands of young girls when he would ask them to exchange the vows of peace. But he came to believe that this was God's way of calling His children close to Him and, thereby, of confirming his own vocation as the priest of Sheshi.

"Not long thereafter, Prefti Vlasë began writing letter after letter to the Bishop in Potenza seeking permission to preach across the seven mountains so that he could spread this newfound message of love to other youths. He sat patiently, in sickness or in health, outside the Church every late afternoon, waiting for the mailman to deliver the Bishop's reply. The passersby soon took pity on the priest, sitting expectantly on his wooden chair, scarcely covered by his black coat in the lazy, cold rains of late November.

"But they soon began to wonder if he had abandoned them. All kinds of herbal teas were brewed to bring the priest back. Nothing worked. The young women who had made preparations for their weddings months in advance could no longer wait for the priest to come to his senses. Angry and impatient, they implored their parents to summon a younger, more capable priest to the village. 'Don't waste your time,' was the answer they received. 'No one will be sent to this village. In a little while you will be able to pray to God through the moving screen with the metal box. You won't even need to go to the priest to receive communion. A piece of bread will have the same effect.'

"The town's mayor had seen the people sing and dance inside a metal box in the big town of the region where they had once gone to sell knives and scissors. He was determined to bring this innovation from Potenza to Sheshi. 'It is about time that we open our eyes to how things are done outside the world of our memories,' he said to the villagers in the café. 'It is for the good of our children, for they will be staying behind when we are gone.'

"At first, the townspeople had no idea of what he was talking about; they assumed that their incomprehension was due to the divide between the speech of the municipal authorities and those of the common folk. The men who conducted business in the town hall were chosen to lead simply because they spoke and wrote a language which had very little to do with the sounds of the four seasons and the changes in color of the wheat fields. Confusion finally took hold of every home in Sheshi. The young ones were having difficulties identifying the sounds with which to name the new objects. They consulted the elders at the bottom of Sheshi. But the old men and women concluded that the new sounds that had taken hold of the village had nothing to do with those with which they were familiar. Not long after, the people of Sheshi spent hours in the main square attempting to communicate their simplest needs and desires. The magic box which the mayor had brought back to the village from Potenza was declared the culprit by the town council of elders, who finally decided to appoint a special commission composed of people of all ages to study and decipher the sounds which emanated from the metal box.

"To many, a trick was involved, since the sounds themselves did not reflect any gesture or feeling which they had ever experienced before. Some felt that the box was a way to keep the young busy and the restless restrained. Many others felt its appearance confirmed the fact that the village had failed to recognize the changes that come with progress. And to the meager few who had always lived by themselves among thousands of books, constantly searching for that one that they could recommend to everyone else, it was a way to erase individual differences. 'In a short while, we are all going to think alike,' warned the one who possessed the rarest book collection in all of Sheshi.

"Sooner than expected, the metal box had entered every home. Explanations for its use were given daily in the square by people dressed in white and black uniforms. Mothers found themselves unable to detach their children from the magical box; even those youngsters with restlessness written all over their foreheads stayed glued to it until the screen began to move with a gentle touch of a key.

"The young went beyond the seven mountains and for the first time measured the width of rivers and the height of endless chains of mountains without actually climbing up to the train station. For the elderly at the bottom of Sheshi, the wandering spirits had taken over. The world they had known but had not finished deciphering was quickly coming to an end. Greetings in the streets were rarely exchanged. The fountain of the fig trees on the road to the wheat fields began to dry. Future brides abandoned their embroidery as they learned that more symmetrical sheets and bedcovers, as well as shiny silverware and soft tablecloths, could be had in places indicated on the magical box.

"The Church of the Dead locked its doors after Prefti Vlasë's internment at the hospice just beyond the village crossroads. In short order it began to show the damaging effects of the rains and the wind. Rats had begun to chew on the few remaining wooden benches infested with black ants.

"From time to time an old disheveled woman could be seen kneeling on what once must have been the high altar. No one, however, was able to identify her, nor did anyone dare to approach her for a good look. Something about her prevented even the most curious from looking directly into her eyes. The children who taunted her with all manner of name-calling found that the rocks they threw at her as she knelt turned into sparrows who took flight in alarm over her head. At night, the woman's piercing cries traveled through every street and up every alley, knocking on every door and filling the people's eyes with floods of tears. Every homeowner put out a piece of bread and a glass of water for her roaming soul. Only with the first streaks of dawn would her penetrating lament die down.

"Finally, those few town's folk who dared to venture from the security of their homes attended a special meeting, where they decided to collect funds from everyone, within the village and beyond it, in order to restore both the Church of the Dead and the former order and civility of Sheshi. Master Nicodemi, whose house sat in a field of red clay at the highest point of the village, was selected to repair the statue of the Virgin Mary with the bloody tears. Master Nicodemi had been the toymaker of all the children of Sheshi for as long as anyone could remember. People said that he always gave a bit of his soul to each of his creations so that they could speak to him during the long winter days.

"The mayor himself, accompanied by his entourage, set out for the ceramist's home to demand that Nicodemi restore the delicate balance between sound, color and feelings to all the damaged statues of the Church of the Dead. When the men were unable to find the right road, they stopped at the barber shop, where the barber gave them an old map made of goat skin. 'Just avoid touching the prickly bushes that enclose his property,' he warned. 'I'll have the boy Zelmi take you up to the lower hill. The house is visible from there.' That was the first time I saw Nicodemi.

"I remember that afternoon very well," asserted Grandfather Zelmi as he held my hand firmly. "The air was redolent with rosemary. It was the season for it to bloom at the foot of the tallest of the seven mountains, and the soft breeze would bring its scent down to the village. That was the signal to climb the mountain and claim the plant with the silver color and pungent odor. The rosemary needles smelled like the air on top of the seven mountains as they dried next to the burning logs of the fireplaces.

"We reached Nicodemi's house at sundown. The ascent was most difficult because of the tall, prickly bushes, known as 'drizët' by the mountain people; all the November rain had caused them to grow into the size of small trees.

"'I shall give orders to burn all this bad brush,' one of them said. I could not tell which one it was, since none of them had said a word to me, but I did see that it was the one who had bloodied his hands far worse than the others because he had taken the lead behind me. From this vantage point I could see the brown rooftops of Sheshi clinging ever so closely to one another, as in the picture which hung over the big bed in our house. That was the picture which I missed the most when I took the train that early morning to go to the big city in the north. The swallows swirling around the main fountain in the square looked like tiny insects, just like the ones I used to see along the brook flying around and around, teasing the fish in the slowly moving water.

"I do not know how he could have known, but Master Nicodemi was waiting for us as we reached the top of the hill. 'I will be ready with the statue of the Crying Mother before Good Friday,' he yelled from in front of his house. His assertive voice and timeless appearance left everyone speechless. 'I will use the dark clay that gathers at the foot of the mountain where the poplars dance in the wind,' he announced. The mayor, by now sweating profusely, asked Nicodemi if he needed any help bringing the statue down to the village. 'I will carry her on my shoulders during Holy Week,' he answered, as he turned to open the door to his stone house with no windows.

"That was the last time I saw Nicodemi, even though I

could still see much of his childlike face in the statue of the Crying Madonna when they carried her through every street of the village looking for her son, as she had done ever since the arrival of the red-bearded refugees from Constantinople.

"Holy Week was a special time in Sheshi," I remember Grandfather Zelmi saying. "For a while, people seemed to become themselves again, pacing back and forth along the main street. The bricklayers were busy restoring the Church of the Dead, which was to receive the Virgin Mother with the tears in her eyes. The women planted the grain seeds that never failed to sprout in green and yellow colors on the Day of the Resurrection. It was time for the children of Sheshi to hide so as not to be seen by the procession of women with disheveled hair and lacerated breasts as they followed the statue of the Crying Virgin. The women of the village dressed in black for nine months of the year, each mourning the death of every child born and yet to come. The women's cries awoke every serpent in the surrounding wheat fields. The meandering snakes en route to the sacred cave gleamed like so many falling stars, awing the people of Sheshi for three days. Black drapes hung from every window and balcony to mitigate the brightness."

Not too long ago, just as the train left the station, my mother asked me not to look back at the village. I did not know then what her motive was. The resigned faces of the middle-aged couple seated across from us told the story of the end of a cycle. But the relived memories with Grandfather Zelmi urged me with their persistence to open the door to them widely.

"I cannot tell you precisely how long we stayed in that isolated corner of the waiting room next to the small coal-burning stove. I covered my face for fear of being recognized by the guard who every now and then peeked inside to make sure that no one had moved from his assigned place. Everyone in that large, windowless corridor stood motionless. I could only see involuntary stirrings whenever the whistle of the locomotive announced the arrival or departure of a train. Nothing more. We were placed in a special area for stranded people.

"Outside, things moved too quickly. I don't think any one of us, sitting where we were, could have dealt with the noise or with the rushing. People outside moved with the precision of a clock as if maneuvered by someone in the station.

"The old man, hiding his dog from the guard, was leaning with his head on my chest, but I could scarcely follow the movement of his breathing. It was very uneven, and at times he gasped more deeply for air.

"I left the waiting room when it was still dark so that I could take my place where I could be most visible to the people looking for day laborers. 'The old man knows that I will be back with a warm bowl of soup, the kind that will ease his breathing.' During the night, the long fingers with which he held the dog had not even twitched, and his coloring had been rather unusual. It had been like that of the sky after one of those storms which would roll over Sheshi in August, snapping all the grapes from their vines. The color, in fact, looked much like that of the statue of Master Nicodemi. Years later, of course, it became clear to me that I had been holding the body of Master Nicodemi in that waiting room.

"That morning I left the waiting room when it was still dark. I remember the heavy air and the bitter cold. The few lights still shining added a deep silence to the street where the long lines of people waiting to be picked up stretched as far as the eyes could see. The men stood like sheep, their heads lowered beneath the incessant raindrops. The sight would have stirred pity and anger in anyone looking at those faceless people, beaten and bent by others' callousness and indifference. Yet there I was, too, waiting to be chosen, by chance, by someone coming from who knew where, someone utterly indifferent to my needs and wants. The image of the old man and his dog cloaked in futility awaited us all. 'We have all been tricked!' I yelled at them, but I did not see one face look up. Swept by a wave of nausea, I stepped out of the line without saying a word. A bitter sensation filled my mouth as I clung to the lamppost. The rain-filled fog rendered the people on line invisible to the drivers speeding by, unconcerned. Their bodies receded into the fog along with the flickering lights drowned by the unrelenting raindrops.

"After a few days of standing in line, I knew that I had to cross the snowcapped mountains to the north of the city to look for work. There, I had heard, one could save enough money to live for months. I was determined not to give in to the resignation I saw in the faces of all of those who stood in line rigidly beneath the beating of the cold rain.

"Two men wearing dark blue uniforms and waving batons in the air crossed into the darkness where the people waited in line. They urged them to move on. Like ants following one another, those in the line dispersed, taking refuge in the open doorways and archways of the side street. Above, the first signs of light were announcing the beginning of a new day, with people moving up and down in measured steps, stopping every now and then in front of a lit window, attracted by the array of things they fancied. Lines crisscrossed, entangling and disentangling from corner to corner. Cars and trucks moved with mathematical precision, turning their signal lights on and off and shooting through the air as if controlled by the round lights of different colors hanging in mid-air. Only years later did I learn that each person inside each automobile carried a sundial that sent messages to the other automobiles. I sat on the steps of a home and thought of your great-grandfather so far away beyond the unending ocean, searching for a home where there were no homes, feeding his long desire to unite his family under the dream of security. Your great-grandmother never failed to remind him that dreams are made of the colors of the rainbow. They vanish before you have a chance to see where they come from. 'They are made to entice the children to fly their kites after the summer rains,' she would say. Somehow your great-grandfather knew he had to shelter his own dream and one day, like so many before him, climb the hill that led to the train station of Sheshi. Now we both know that no one escapes from that compulsion to go beyond the seven mountains. For some the stay in distant lands is short; for others, it is as long as a life time. But they all come back to make certain that the village will go on living its eternal dream of building homes of memories beyond the infinite horizons of time."

The train came out of the last tunnel and went by an abandoned train station without reducing its speed. Grandfather Zelmi's memories were as clear as the resigned punishment on the faces of the elderly couple sitting in front of us.

"I walked back to the waiting room of the train station. It was completely deserted. The many tracks that faced the station were empty. Garbage cans were lying empty with the refuse scattered on the pavement. The wind whistled as it passed from one arch to another, swirling newspapers into the air. I dragged myself to the waiting room with a feeling of apprehension. The hall, too, was completely empty. I fixed my eyes on the corner where I had left the old man with the dog, but I only saw the scarf he had used to cover the dog. I ran outside the station only to face an icy wind and walls of water. That night, I ran for a long time, hoping to find the old man and his dog.

"I woke up inside a small truck with many other people inside. They were mostly young with fearful eyes and rigid hands. I was as frightened as they were. We all knew not where we were going. The women, with heads covered by black shawls, sat cross-legged as they held their children, still tender in age. Passive and despondent, they clung to their husbands as if they wanted to share the fear of uncertainty and the trepidation of the moment. The truck was unbearably cold. We must have been traveling through the snowy mountains, for, at times, I could hear the sound of rushing water on our side, like the water I would hear in Sheshi after a heavy rainfall that brought down from the mountains everything it could find in its path.

"Indeed, those were terrible events in Sheshi. The ones who suffered the most were the peasants who lived down in the flatlands. After the storm everyone would go down into the ravines to see what they could salvage among the dead animals. A lamb or a goat could be found alive, shrinking against a cliff. For most, it was the beginning of a hard life ahead. They gathered what they could and began rebuilding their huts. For the others, and especially for the young ones who had no patience, it was time to climb the hill that lead to the train station.

"At this very moment I could see the same look of desperation in the faces in front of me. 'We are all searching for something better than what we left behind,' the one whose eyes had the shape of two daggers murmured softly. The people in the truck had dark brown skin and long thick black hair plaited in braids. They were rather small in stature and held their young wrapped in colorful woolen mantles. They must have been on the road for months. Each family shared grains of corn they carried in a small leather sack. Each face bore an air of passivity, an atavistic patience. I offered them the piece of bread I had saved from the refectory. The smile I received from the head of the family was to stay with me for the rest of time. The smile had all the innocence of childhood rescued from oblivion.

"From the small opening in the canvas cover of the truck I could see a chain of mountains with clouds resting on their peaks. They were taller than our seven mountains whose movements and shifts in search of the sun I followed from the stone steps of the Church of the Dead in Sheshi. I thought of the hour before sunset when the mountain peaks turned into little colored boats with white sails flying towards the endless horizons but always coming back to rest at the earliest signs of dawn.

"It was the time when the fields were filled with infinite colors bedazzling the flowered fruit trees, with the red of poppies and with the yellow of the sprouting wheat. The air smelled of spring. The somnolent odor was carried to the main square of Sheshi by the soft breeze that came from where the sun rises in the morning. Every door and window of the homes was opened to harness as much of the perfumed air as possible. The young girls opened the small bottles they had saved and filled them with the precious aroma. They hid the bottles in their dolls' dresses, fearful of being caught growing up too fast without the consent of their parents. It was a game they played with deftness and precision to keep one world from ever infringing upon the other. The elders of the village were the only ones who could follow the movement of the young from the fields of childhood imagination to the confined space of the main square. The grandmothers would soon summon the white-haired woman outside the ancient cave of the serpents who bathed the girls in water filled with rose petals, cut her long and disheveled hair and exposed her breasts bursting with life. The girls were then instructed to jump three times over their rag dolls for which they had cared throughout their tender years. The thirty-three needles placed in the doll's heart were then removed carefully, avoiding any lacerations. Aided by their grandmothers, who had been following the ceremony at a distance, each of the girls would then choose a spot to bury her doll. Thenceforth, she would begin to tie her hair into knots and she would resolve to no longer look at people in their eyes.

"I wondered if the woman who sat across from me, gently inclined against her husband's shoulders, had ever lifted her eyes. The tenderness with which she held her child was reminiscent of the statue of the Crying Madonna on the niche next to the altar of the Church of the Dead. That mother understood the people so well. At times, she was heard to speak to them softly, barely moving her lips as the faithful knelt in front of her. It was said in Sheshi that she had a special place in her big red heart filled with needles for everyone in need. Old Elías, the village storyteller, would get his stories from her. 'She is full of heartbeats,' he maintained. 'Each pounding of the heart reveals a line of a story that has no end and I share them with you so that her heart never stops beating. You must do the same as you grow up and take the road up to the train station.'

"Old Elías, as the rest of the people in the village, understood that every young man, sooner or later, would leave the village. 'Our village gives life and waits patiently to receive it at the end when there are no more roads to follow.' Old Elías's words were as clear as a spring day after a downpour.

"I sat in that cold, damp truck and realized how the distance from one's place of birth sharpens the eyes and stimulates the mind. Old Elías knew deep in his memories what awaited each of those straightforward faces that listened to his stories. I could tell by the way he gazed into our eyes, reading in them what was to happen and only allowing a tear or two to fill his eyes.

"Old Elías would always be the first one at the train station to say good-bye to the departing young man with the saddest look and a trembling handshake. He left the train station only when the train dove deeply into the darkness of the tunnel.

"Each departure was followed by days of silence in the village during which the people walked with their eyes lowered to the ground. Although the children still imitated the flight of the swallows in front of the fountain and the adults, dressed as always with their starched collars rigidly tied around their necks, came down to the square in search of a cool breeze, the latter avoided coming face to face with one another for fear of showing the tears forming in their eyes. Indeed, the elders often went to the fountain that stood between the two giant fig trees to wash the sadness from their eyes while pretending to check the ripeness of the fruit.

"The melancholia that had taken over the village affected even the few remaining swallows. In those days, they were rarely seen diving and swirling in the air with the sound of the bells. The air filled, instead, with the moans of the dead escaping from the crevices of the tombs in the mausoleums. The night belonged to the departed souls. The sign of the cross was placed on every door and prayers were said for those souls still unable to detach themselves from the warmth and memories and breath of their kin. Many a time, deep scratches were found on every door in Sheshi. It was a strange, indecipherable language. People said that they were the scratches made by the wolves that searched for the warmth of the fireplaces.

"The winters seemed never to come to an end with so many people gone across the ocean. But it was when the wheat fields were emblazoned in yellow that the women felt their husbands' absence. The oldest of the seventeen elders was sent around the village to announce that it was time to cut the wheat and to prune the olive trees for the fall harvest.

"Old Elías spent the winter days reading and interpreting the letters the people of Sheshi received from their sons and husbands. He showed me the strange looking people and animals on the postage of the envelopes and told me that one day I also would have to go to the city of the blue seas. 'There,' he said, with the sadness lodged permanently in his eyes, 'you will get the boat that will take you to the city of dreams and where books that carry pictures of the places and people in the world are kept. You have to find the right one. Many of the books are covered in dust; others have faded words and still others have words that hide so far beyond one's depth that you will need a concave glass to fetch them from the deep. They call the place "Arcana Imperi." People go in one by one and they hold onto a white string that glows in the dark. That is the only way they can find their way back to the starting point. I have been told that many never do find their way back because they let go of the string and are then bewitched by the power of the words which lock them in never ending intersecting caves.'

"Old Elías always interpreted the letters in ways that would have pleased the anxious parents and wives. 'I am working very hard and there is nothing that I desire that

I cannot have,' he read to all of them. Hearing such words from their loved ones made their hearts pound a little less fitfully. Soon enough, Old Elías's home began to fill with sacks of dried fruits and olives. The content of the letters, and the references to things never seen in Sheshi, filled me with a gnawing, inner curiosity that Old Elías did not fail to notice. 'You will know when your time to leave the village is near.'

"I remember well that it was at this time that I felt a pain in one of my shoes that increased unbearably as I passed under the window of Anastasia, your grandmother. It was a small stone that turned into a prickly needle when I looked at her ashen face. 'You are turning into a man,' your great-grandmother told me when I mentioned the pain to her. 'There is no stone inside your shoe, so don't waste your time looking for one.'

"Months later, I realized that the pain inside the shoe had developed an echo in my heart. 'I planted it there,' Anastasia wrote on the flowered paper she threw at me as I stood underneath her window waiting anxiously to glimpse her face. 'Don't lose the paper, for it has the perfume of the flowers that grow down in the ravine. It will remind you of me and the flowers that only open their petals to the full moon.'

"I woke up tightly holding the amulet that your great-grandmother had saved for me with the Madonna of Constantinople and the flowered letter of Anastasia. I saved that amulet for you. You will recognize it by the shiny button in the shape of a heart in the middle of it. 'Always keep the amulet with you,' Old Elías said to me when I showed it to him. 'When you long for the village, you have only to touch it and close your eyes. You will find yourself at once at the old fountain where everyone comes to collect the water in their jars. Their faces tell the story of Sheshi, and they move easily from one side of the fountain to the other. It is the desire to see what lies behind the fountain that draws everyone back to the village. The journey will be long or short; no one knows. But they all end up here no matter where they have been.'

"The truck bumped over the rocky road. Piles of debris massed against the edges of the road and the rain fell on top of the truck like the hail of an August storm. They had been traveling for two days and two nights. The driver shouted and cursed at every jolt. The men kept a close watch on their women. At night they huddled around the fire and were told not to fall asleep. Their eyes filled with the kind of fear that I had seen on the faces of the people in our village as the torrents of water which came from the mountains year after year washed away all they possessed.

"It must have been late during the third night that the unthinkable happened. The full moon had lodged itself over the camp. Bottles of a white-colored alcohol shone like mirrors in the moonlight. The caravan of people stood close to one another, forming one big black shadow between the burning pile of wood and the ever clearer moonlight. I had taken a place further from the spot where the fire burned slowly. The rain had turned the night into a cold, clear canvas of stars. They were to cross the border before the first rays of light. Even from a distance I could sense the fear that enveloped each family, bathed in the sad moonlight, as the fire slowly died down.

"I saw a woman leaving one of the clusters of families. Her children must have been sound asleep on her husband's lap. She moved slowly towards the woods, trying to suffocate the sound made by her walking shoes. I made nothing of it until I heard a piercing cry rend the stillness of the night. I rushed to the woods and saw the husband now consoling his wife, who was still holding the bloody rock in her hand. On the ground, with his face covered in blood which still gushed from his wounds, lay the truck driver, recognizable only by his multicolored shoelaces. Not a word was spoken.

"For the rest of the night we waited for dawn. We were going to cross the border on foot. I placed the youngest one of the family on my shoulders; throughout the whole ordeal he did not whisper a word as his mother, watching him fixedly, followed us with great trepidation. Yet there was no power anywhere that could have stopped that woman with the curly black hair from crossing the rocky brook and moving with difficulty through the thick woods to the other side of the frontier.

"I could see the rays of the sun shooting like arrows through the dense foliage. The caravan people scattered upon reaching the asphalt road. I arrived at a stone farmhouse with a white wooden fence in front of the entrance. There a red-haired, rather tall man motioned me to follow him to the rear barn. It became clear that he was used to receiving clandestine workers at the farm that was to be my place during my stay in that land on the other side of the snow-capped mountains. I did not even have time to ask his name. He told me not to make myself visible during the morning hours when the local officials made their rounds checking for illegal workers. I helped with the harvest of beets and potatoes just before the first frost. The fields were coated with a fresh sheet of ice as fall was living its last days.

"During the long winter days I thought of the fear in the faces of those strangers inside the truck. I felt the weight of their wanderings and the laments of their mutilated voices. They had traveled over seas and mountains to reach what they were told would be the 'promised land.' The stories that

I had heard in the barber shop died in the peak of winter. The nights are still filled with their distant faces and their pleas still go unheard.

"You should keep alive their memories as I have done when I am gone," Grandfather Zelmi said to me with an unusual assertiveness. Grandfather Zelmi closed his eyes forever with the fall of the first snows.

Chapter Five

Soon after, Father announced his intention to join his sister in America and get the family out of Sheshi. "There is no more space for us in this village," he announced to each of us as if expecting comfort. It was not until much later that I managed to bridge together Grandfather Zelmi's accounts and Father's desire to join his sister in the lands across the ocean. The bridge grew stronger and stronger with the passing of time. People say that bridges and pictures have a life of their own, and so it happened in our home in Sheshi. Mother began to fill the small dresser she kept next to the balcony with all the pictures she could dig out of her wooden chest.

"In every picture there is that special moment that was just able to escape the pounding of the clock in front of the municipal building," she would say to us, and we could glimpse in her face the vanishing smiles and the approaching sadness.

While the village clock on the municipal building continued to relentlessly move on with the precision of former decades, Mother, my younger brother and I found ourselves in the waiting room of the train station on top of the hill. Sheshi was awakening from its nocturnal frozen landscape and was preparing to nestle itself under the first rays of the rising sun. The clouds that during the night had spanned the breadth of the sky and had encircled every rooftop quickly vanished. The lights of the village flickered shyly in the winding streets as the homes unwove mantles of stars from their windows.

It had been during such a morning not long before that I had watched descend into the square of Sheshi a lone woman, her gaze speechlessly intent upon the cupola of stars lingering over the town. On another such morning, a soft breeze wafted into the square, carrying upon it the scent of the eucalyptus which grew in the groves at the side of the road connecting the village with the train station. The whistle of the eight o'clock train from the East announced the beginning of the day to the young men sitting outside the café. Women dressed in black moved silently along the walls, covering their lips and unperturbed by the sound of the doors being opened for the day. Two elderly people greeted one another with a trembling handshake. I sat on the steps of the Church of the Dead, hoping to discern the hidden soul of Sheshi. The elderly, who sat unmoved on the wooden bench under the almond tree, swore that they could see the soul of the village wander through the streets in the dark of the night caressing the stones and lacing the stars over the harvested wheat fields where the red poppies had played and sung with the wind. The square became coated with the stillness of the night, and a grazing silence enveloped the top of the almond trees, stirred only by the sound of the striking hour over the municipal building. It was at this hour that the elderly unfailingly sensed the shadowy figure of Edvige returning from the cemetery along the tall pine trees.

Many a time Edvige had told Mother of her encounters with her dead son; she related his plans to return to the village on moonless nights. Mother had listened attentively, making certain to betray no sign of disbelief. "He is too lonely," Edvige would confide, "and he misses the smell of the chestnuts roasting on the fire during the Christmas season."

Edvige did not miss a day going to the cemetery to assuage her son's loneliness. In the village everyone knew the spot where her son, Miklini, was buried, because the flowers

Edvige had planted there that day had never withered. Neither the intense heat of summer nor the heavy snows of the winter months could affect them. However, no one in the village found these circumstances unusual, knowing, as they did, the special powers which Edvige possessed to read the ways of nature. The elderly in the square, who had known Edvige since the beginning of their memories, felt that it was only a matter of time before she would find the formula to bring her only son back from the dead. With this conviction in mind, the village folk took seriously everything she said, particularly the dreams she related.

Every Sunday, after the midday Mass, Edvige, dressed in her best attire, sat outside her one-room home, interpreting the inexplicable dreams that everyone brought to her. These personal confessions ended only when the village clock struck midnight. The last to come to see Edvige were always the future brides and those at the threshold of womanhood. Edvige knew every one of them, but she never spoke of their intimate needs to anyone else.

During his lifetime, Miklini was not aware of his mother's special powers. But he did notice, as he played with others of his age or as he sat on the front steps of the café where he often listened to the tales told by those who had returned from faraway places, that people seemed to distance themselves from him. Miklini gave this no particular attention until he set his eyes on the face of a young girl more or less his age. Every afternoon after that first encounter, at exactly five o'clock, she passed by the café on her way to the fountain to draw fresh water for her father. The girl had no Christian name. Her mother, not wanting to offend any of the relations, simply called her "Dheu." This was a name no one could find in any book. Even Prefti Vlasë could not locate it in any of the Christian name books he possessed. The caretaker of the church felt that the name was locked in the deepest recesses of the mind. "Her eyes are like towers of sounds," he told Prefti Vlasë soon after the baptismal ceremony.

On a clear autumn afternoon, as Dheu passed by the café, she blinded everyone else present except Miklini. The latter, more determined than ever, rose from his chair and followed the angelic figure which was floating over the cobblestones that stretched from the café to the edge of the fountain. For many months thereafter, the two walked together to the fountain, filled the jug with water, and conversed for as long as it took without anyone's noticing the passing of time. From her home, Edvige had succeeded in locking time inside a terra cotta jug filled with water and ashes. The potion confused every clock in the village. The hands marking the hours were unable to distinguish them, and the swallows encircling the bell tower froze over the Church of the Dead.

Shortly, Dheu and Miklini were sharing every moment of the day and night without any villager's even noticing their languid desire for one another. But the trees and the wildflowers that defined the wheat fields on the outskirts of Sheshi brought forth their very best colors, and their aromas intensified as the young lovers became ever more intimate.

This love went on for many months, indeed for many years. Although the seasons came and left with their usual regularity, only Edvige noticed the small imprints of their presence. The rest of the villagers, afflicted by a sort of stupor, kept on living without the municipal clock striking its hours.

On the day that Edvige attempted to lift the veil of timelessness from the youthful faces of Dheu and Miklini, she realized that she no longer had the powers of the past.

One windy morning in late autumn, the people of the village awoke to hear Edvige howling at the fountain of the ancient fig tree. Her piercing moans penetrated every house in Sheshi and pulled everyone into the main square. At the foot of the fig tree, its bark completely charred, stood Miklini, his eyes wide open. In his right hand, some divined the most beautiful red rose they had ever beheld. "As red as the ripest pomegranate," they said.

Many of the elders, called to witness the miracle, felt that this was just one more of those magic tricks which Edvige performed so well. But the younger ones felt unexplained tears spring into their eyes. For the first time they sensed in that red rose the other side of things which stays well inside a person and cannot be shared. The mothers felt that in that charred figure Edvige had met her own fate; she would be destined to spend the rest of her days old and alone with no one to care for her. In spite of numerous investigations involving dogs and tape measures of all kinds, the authorities could find no cause for Miklini's death. Until the day she herself died, Edvige wandered through the streets murmuring to those she met that her son was preparing for his return to Sheshi. She made sure to exhort the people at the café to leave an empty chair for him.

Within a few years, the people of the town no longer paid any attention to Edvige. The elders were convinced that her mind was no longer part of theirs, preoccupied as she was with trying to forget her grief. But the caretaker of the Church of the Dead, whose childlike face seemed to have skirted the ravages of the town's clock since he had climbed the bell tower and refused to abandon it, yelled down to Prefti Vlasë that he often saw Edvige walk from the cemetery to the old chapel carved under the mountain with her son. "It happens when I ring the bells for the six o'clock

Mass. The two of them walk as if they were one. Then they take leave of one another by waving a white handkerchief."

"The Devil is upon us!" screamed Prefti Vlasë in terror. Erlind, the caretaker, took care to never relay his observations or his conversation with the prelate to anyone else. He did not want to be compelled to descend from the place he called home.

Edvige never missed one of her visits to the cemetery until the day before Christmas. It was a cold morning with a few flakes of snow here and there playing with a small number of swallows that had forgotten their way back to the shores of North Africa. Edvige had put on her wedding dress, mostly eaten by moths but still with the memory of the clear blue color that had caught everyone's eye during the wedding celebration at the Church of the Virgin of Constantinople. She moved slowly through the main square accompanied by the silver light of the almond trees. Her eighty years fell to the ground as leaves in late autumn. She reached the fountain and washed her hands but once. A yellow halo followed her as she moved on, leaving behind an odor of burned chestnuts. Edvige had roasted them, one by one, the night before, covering each with oregano leaves just the way her son had preferred them during the winter nights at home next to the fireplace.

The news of the approaching death of Edvige, remembered by some, forgotten by most, spread quickly throughout the village. In no time, every woman left whatever she had been doing, dressed in black, and took her place behind the slowly moving, ethereal figure of Edvige. They formed a solemn, silent procession behind the woman who had brought each of them to life and who knew their deepest, most hidden secrets better than even their closest of kin.

No one found anything astounding in the blue snow flakes that fell that day on the road that led to the cemetery. The long line of women grew yet longer as they neared the Church of the Three Crosses midway between Sheshi and the Abode of the Dead. The women kneeled and beat their breasts as Edvige slowly assumed the shape of the great serpent of her great-great-grandmother. Of all the women present, only the youngest witnessed this transformation, but she was so awestruck by the event that fear closed her vocal chords, rendering her incapable of relating it.

Edvige was laid to rest next to Miklini. In just a few years, this spot became the place where all the young women around the village whispered their most mysterious desires. Somehow, word of Edvige's death reached faraway places beyond the great oceans, and it was not long before money began pouring into the post office of Sheshi. It was to fund the construction of a marble mausoleum with a fountain inside to keep bright and fresh the flowers on top of the tomb.

Sheshi tripled in size. It became necessary to build a ten-foot wall to protect the tomb from the ever growing number of worshippers who came to touch it. Hospices and sanitariums sprouted like dandelions in the early days of spring. At the village café, there were nightly complaints about the unending whistle of the train and the noise from the hourly arrivals of travelers. The young, dazzled by the looks and the wealth of the newcomers, stopped going to the fields to till the land. Rather, they stood in line for hours trying to catch a glimpse of the new faces on their way to the cemetery. In just a few months, Sheshi was transformed from a sleepy village into a bustling town. The train station was given a new look with freshly imported paint from Mexico, and marble moldings from Carrarra were added to every door and window. The train platform was filled with flowers, and small pine trees were planted in light brown ceramic vases imported from Portugal. In fact, the change was so complete that many of the villagers trying to return home did not get off at the train station at all because they did not think that it was their stop.

It came to pass that the people of Sheshi themselves had difficulties in recognizing one another. The strangers coming to town spent mountains of coins, forcing the store owners to spend hours counting them each night and to rack their brains for places to store them safely. Paper money no longer circulated because the merchants, suspicious of the foreign pilgrims, refused to accept it. Caravans of mules arrived daily, bringing sacks of exotic goods from the furthest corners of the world. Finally the mayor ordered that a large shed with a zinc roof be built to keep the animals away from the narrow streets and the open fields of Sheshi.

The elderly inhabitants hid in their homes with their days of old and their memories refilled with stories, so the wooden bench under the almond trees in the square remained empty. The women were afraid to walk through the streets, now crammed with strangers who spoke by rolling their tongues or by spitting fire from their mouths. If they ventured out at all, it was when their husbands accompanied them to fill their jugs with water.

"This pandemonium cannot go on forever," old Tuci whispered to Nicodemi as the two, unique in their boldness, sat in front of the café.

"They will be crushed by the weight of their coins, and we won't even be able to give them a proper burial," his companion replied.

But the town officials, insensitive to the fears of the elders, turned off the last few flickering lights, preparing for the roar of the next day. I got up from the steps of the Church of the Dead and took to the road closest to where I had been sitting so as not to lose sight of Tuci and Nicodemi pursued by the fog. Their home was on the other side of the village. The night seemed in no hurry to reach its resting place. The square was completely deserted, with only a cat or two furtively moving along the encircling walls. I could sense the weight of the silence upon my shoulders and, as the road grew steeper, I could not move my legs. I searched for a place to stop and catch my breath, but darkness shaded my eyes.

Awaking, I know not when, I felt the heat of the early afternoon. "They found you asleep as the field workers were climbing up towards the chestnut groves," Mother explained, not mentioning them by name. The church bells were announcing someone's death. "They are ringing for Nicodemi," Mother said in a firm voice. "They found him hanging by the olive tree last night. May he find a place to rest in the deepest caves of the earth after all his wandering." I realized that it must have been Nicodemi who could not go through the fog.

Knowing how much I liked to listen to Nicodemi's stories, my mother had cautioned "One of these days he is going to fill your head with butterflies that will take you to the train station and away from home." When I replied "He has seen what we will never see unless we leave the village," Mother's face had turned pale. I can still see her distress as if it were happening today. What frightened her was my determination to follow in the footsteps of her father. She had already lost a husband and dreaded to let go of a son. "One should stay where one has first felt the rays of the sun and smelled the dampness of the earth. Your father has probably lost his way back home. He has been away too long."

The church bells rang with renewed force, penetrating through every opening of the house. Prefti Vlasë tried in vain to persuade Erlind to come down from the bell tower, but the caretaker only jumped on and off the bell as it moved from one side to the other, clinging to it like a vine to a wall. The ringing continued with even greater passion after the quick burial of Nicodemi by the few people who still remembered him.

Prefti Vlasë refused to allow the coffin into the church. "Suicide is contrary to nature and therefore sinful," he explained to the angry crowd outside his home. "Make certain that he goes back to the womb of the earth before sunset." The priest was concerned that Nicodemi's soul would not let him sleep as it wandered through the village sighing for a place to rest.

I did not tell them of Nicodemi's desire to be buried next to the barren fig tree which he had planted at the side of his home because Nicodemi had taken with him the secret road to his house. Instead, he was laid to rest in a remote corner outside the walls of the cemetery. A small wooden cross marked the spot, with neither name nor age carved upon it. Years later, as the seasons grew shorter, Sheshi forgot the spot where Nicodemi had been buried, for the wooden cross had decayed without a trace. As the need for space grew, the guardian of the cemetery, who knew exactly where each one was buried, attempted many a time but to no avail to break the ground where Nicodemi rested. "The ground outside the wall of the cemetery is as hard as a rock," he complained to the people in the café. When he observed "We are going to have to bring in heavy machinery from the big city," the others thought he was lying, but the lack of vegetation and the infrequent rains had indeed turned the ground into stone.

The bearded old men who sat alone on the wooden bench of the square had spoken, in the past, of the name of the person buried underneath the site of the heavy stones, but the name brought back no memories. One by one the remaining few who could have recalled Nicodemi's existence had left the village. Some had taken the train and never returned. Others had sailed for the fresh waters of the Amazon to mine gold from the shores of the river. For a long time, the old bearded man who rested his chin on his wooden cane as he counted the swallows flying in the sky was the only one left whose memories could bring Nicodemi back to life. He had written Nicodemi's name and the date of his burial on a piece of sheepskin and had placed it inside a blue glass bottle on a day when the almond trees had begun to shed their leaves. During the last days of fall, protected by the carpet of leaves, old Tuci descended to the ancient cave and hid the blue bottle in the stream that fed the fountain of the dead. It was the only way to lessen the sadness of forgetfulness that had been afflicting everyone in the village. The disease finally made its way into the placid waters of memories.

It was during this time that Mother had fallen into a deep silence. What allowed her to keep in touch with the few objects still in the house was the letter from Father that the postman never failed to deliver on the first Friday of the month. Father's neat handwriting was what brought her back to the time of yesterday. The piercing lament heard many times before, especially in the first year of his departure, had turned into a feebler moaning. "Your father is getting older," she whispered one day as I read the last letter delivered to her. "He writes with a trembling hand and the paper no longer smells of wild flowers."

In the spring came a letter sealed with black asphalt. We were to go the city asleep under the volcano for medical examinations and for verification of documentation and eventual entry into the land beyond the great ocean. The postman, in his best uniform, had come in person to deliver the sealed envelope. "It comes from a special office," he remarked, "and you must put a cross on the spot where I am pointing."

In Mother's eyes I could see a nascent sparkle of the joy that had been there in the days before Father's decision to take my older brother and sister with him to join his own sister in the "promised land" beyond the ocean. For a moment the desire to see her husband and her older children overruled her fear of leaving the village. "A woman's place is with her husband," she said to me in a voice that betrayed her need to justify leaving the house.

That night she did not close her eyes. I watched her staring persistently at the slow-burning flame from the few charred logs in the fireplace. The night had turned especially cold and the wind was constantly knocking the window pane against the balcony. I spent the night thinking of the wild flowers we had placed over the mound of dirt where Nicodemi was purported to have been buried. The howling wind must have swept them away together with the wooden cross. For the first time I felt a cold sweat descending through my fingers, numbing them. I recalled what Grandfather Zelmi had told me of the many cold nights he had spent in the big city of the north. "You will never know when estrangement will take possession of you. Loneliness and fear always come together, and they bring the dread of faraway skies. Suddenly you can no longer feel your fingers."

Mother had begun to mutter something to herself. I

could feel the vibrations of her wrangling mind from where I lay. During that night that never seemed to come to an end, I kept looking for the first rays of sunlight that worked their way into the house from the balcony each morning. Finally the crowing of the roosters gave me assurance that the sun had indeed managed to break through the clouds, sending thousands of ships filled with butterflies to summon the peasants to the fields.

No longer sparkling, as they had so briefly the night before, my mother's eyes had turned black and swollen after spending so many hours lost in thought while staring at the burning log. Mother now prepared the usual cup of coffee.

The dusty road that connected Sheshi to the distant wheat fields still yielded up the piercing cries of the dead German soldiers. The village lived in dire poverty for many years. "Milk is for those who want soft skin," Mother said to us. Mothers, young and old, fed on wild grasses and sold their belongings to strangers for a bushel of grain. "Things will change when the men come back," the women would say. It was their way of consoling one another. It was at that time that I came to distinguish among the people of Sheshi according to what they were able to buy from those strangers who came to town once a week. Seeds and anger mixed with a deep mistrust had been sown in the village. The people had devised ways of greeting and speaking without revealing anything about themselves. Sheshi had descended into the cave of deep silences.

The day we received the letter from the consulate from the city by the sea was the day that the padlock was set on the door to our home. I myself felt a sort of inner freedom and a sense of adventure which the people of Sheshi did not fail to see. It must have been the way I walked through the square and looked at the almond trees. I had been told not to raise my eyes, not to look directly into the eyes of others. I always carried a book with me and looked for places to store the names of characters that floated through the pages. I can still recall, though my eyes are now blurred, the snowflakes that danced with the wind the day we set out for the white building of the foreign consulate. We had joined the unending line of people from the village who searched night and day for ways to escape from their inner prisons and find the secret tunnel through the seven mountains. The world on the other side of the barrier weighed heavily on their minds. The desire did not spare anyone. It was the curse that mothers feared the moment they saw their sons leave the womb. It must have been what punished Mother as she sat next to the fire the night we received the letter.

The next morning the sun rose, tinged in red and yellow. The recently planted wheat fields down the narrow brook glistened like so many stars shooting their arrows through the hazy horizon. I had saved the smell of the earth bathed in the early morning dew in an envelope. The waiting room of the train station in Sheshi seemed emptier than before even with the four of us there. Three nights before, I had gone to see my great-great-grandmother at the very end of the village. I had asked her to interpret the recurrent dream of a big city with glassy buildings as tall as the smallest of the seven mountains and with rivers of people walking in straight lines and with movements as regulated as those of the puppets in the carnival that visited the village for two nights every year.

"I know why you came to see me," she murmured as she continued to feed more kindling into the fire where a pot of water was boiling. "I will consult the well of memories," she added, "provided that there are no stars in the sky. The light from the heavens burns my skin and dries my eyes." After that, she said no more.

The winds outside seemed to pick up more and more strength. For the past few years they had grown in ferocity, making the houses tremble and lifting the trees into the air, roots and all. To Mother, bad times awaited the village. Her deep red eyes followed the howling wind through every street of Sheshi.

That night, I left my great-great-grandmother's house with an inexplicable sense of loss. I had not been able to extract from her words the interpretation I had sought. In the morning, I gathered the last figs of the season to take to her so that she might dry them for the winter.

"I wept all night long with your ancestors," she cried the minute I opened the door. "Your grandfather had tears that carved wounds upon his cheeks as they fell. He fears that you will be lost on a long trip to a very different land where the earth won't taste of anything and the air will smell of rotten eggs. What is worse," she continued, "where you are going, the streets will be lined with mirrors that enclose people, preventing them from ever getting close to one another. You must keep your memories alive, for they will prevent the mirrors from multiplying your image until you can no longer recognize yourself. I will give you a small pouch filled with a few seeds surrounded by earth from the waters that spring from the sacred cave." She pressed my pulse with her hand, fusing her heart beat with mine. My arm tingled all the way to my neck, as if I were being bitten by a swarm of bees.

That evening I returned home, determined not to mention any of this to my mother. The streets were deserted, although the doors to the homes had been left ajar so that the villagers could hear the beasts of burden tied to the front wall. The train station upon the hill was filled with an air of

131

desolation and loneliness as a few dogs roamed aimlessly along the stony road. Clouds dipped in wet silences descended from the seven mountains as the sun began to set.

I thought of Grandfather Zelmi in that remote corner of the cemetery and of his journey up north. I was, perhaps, the only one in the village ever to have known of his venture outside of Sheshi. With regret, I recalled his deep desire to share with me the bits of his life. I tried to patch together the pieces as one would struggle to keep old photographs from fading away. In the distance, the tall pine trees in the sacred soil stood taller and greener than ever.

Mother had taken in the vases of flowers from the balcony of our home. We were to leave to join Father as soon as the notice arrived from Naples. In the square, night forced the almond trees to cling together as morning dew grips thirsty leaves. The women at the fountain basin drew water for their laundry. The men sat outside the café as Aristi began to unfold the chairs for the night's gathering. The steps to the Church of the Dead shone in hues of blue and gray which had provided a sense of security to all who had touched them. Hidden rays emanated from those stones and traveled through the village from North to South. The marvel had been told and retold by the ancients for centuries. "Those steps hold the invisible footprints of every wandering soul since the beginning of time, connecting the spirit of the square to the ritual of the jugs filled with water at the fountain and to the gates of the cemetery." The very heat of the stones traveled through underground brooks, brightening the painted murals on the walls of the ancient Church of Saint Leonard and protecting the villagers on their way to the wheat fields.

At home, everything was made ready for our departure.

Each piece of furniture passed down from generation to generation was labeled to go to close relatives who had come of age to the surprise of the neighbors. The news spread rapidly throughout the village that two female relatives were now ready to attract serious suitors. The white-washed walls of our house, stripped of the few pictures they had held and of the few pieces of furniture which had been set in the corners, now looked abject. Blackened by the smoke from the chimney, the walls shed dark tears through the crevices.

I gathered the three books I possessed and tied them together with a shoelace I had saved. The books had provided a window on the world outside of Sheshi. The long winter days under the heavy snows had been made shorter and less unforgiving by the colors and sounds arrayed in their pages. I had promised Grandfather Zelmi that I would take good care of them, endeavoring to find every secret they hid. "Those books can show you the way out of the boredom that afflicts everyone in Sheshi." Those words, which, at that time had made little sense to me, now became the impetus behind the destined journey.

The last week at the house was spent mostly in silence. The hours seemed to go even more slowly than usual. The bit of sky I could see from the balcony was a mixture of gray and orange. The wind which had been bellowing all night long had swept away the threatening black clouds.

Not long after, a sharp knock at the door startled Mother from her stupor. My uncle had come to Sheshi to accompany us to the train station. His companion, a German shepherd who never left his sight, took his place at the entrance to the house. "I have come to take you to the train station," Uncle Karmel announced.

Uncle Karmel was a man of very few words, a tiny figure of a person whose name still reminded the village elders of the horrors of the last war. Everyone knew him in the village because of the odor of burned flesh he carried with him until his death. Father had cautioned me never to mention the war in his presence. "Your uncle is alive today because of a stroke of luck," he told me one afternoon as we watched him walking all alone towards the hill overlooking Sheshi. "He had been caught by the Germans and condemned to be shot with thirty-three other men of the village. He must have fallen before the bullets could actually reach his body, knocked down by the other less fortunate men who were felled in the hail of bullets. At dusk, the German soldiers loaded all the bodies onto a wooden cart and brought them to be burned in a gravel pit outside the cemetery. There he was able to hide among the dead and escape when the soldiers left to fetch the gasoline. On that same day Uncle Karmel joined a group of partisans in the south. Years after the war ended the people of Sheshi, who had gone out to look for him, found him by following a trail of smoking powder. It was said that he had avenged every one of the men shot and then had buried the weapon. From then on, Uncle Karmel ceased to speak with the people of Sheshi."

Identifying the season through its scent in the air, Uncle Karmel came down to Sheshi from his mountain hideout once or twice a year to visit his mother. He still instilled fear and respect in those villagers who had lived the events of the Great War. It was during one of those appearances that I saw Uncle Karmel for the first time. Having stopped at the café to savor a cup of black coffee, he sat all alone in the corner. Izmir, the old man with the eyes of a hawk, who always measured the height and weight of things from a distance and never missed in his appraisal, approached me and whispered in my ear. "That man who sits all alone in the corner is your uncle. He comes to visit his aged mother and to make certain that he does not forget anyone in the village. People say that you should not look into his eyes, for he could snatch the soul right out of your body. You see how dark his skin is? That is because he has been to Hell and back!"

Uncle Karmel's looks did indeed resemble those of the Devil who never ceased to scream under the foot of Saint George in the icon opposite the main altar in the Church of the Dead. Women always made the sign of the cross and closed their eyes as they passed beneath this image. The young ran in front on their way to catechism class for fear of being transfixed by those eyes.

The morning of our departure my uncle came dressed in an army uniform he had taken from a German soldier. During the last days of the war, the German had lost his way back to his regiment. As we climbed silently toward the train station, I felt the piercing edges of the stones lying on the road. The clock on the municipal building was enveloped by the fading light of the moon. The houses, still deep in slumber within the last moments of the night, were unaware of the faint pink hues on the horizon. At the lower part of Sheshi, flocks of sheep moved like white dots in search of the little grass that might have grown during the night.

I glanced in the direction of the cemetery where the night was still closely packed in black. The tall pine trees, barely visible, were caped in silence. I thought of Nicodemi, still restless in his final resting place.

At the entrance to the tunnel, a group of men had begun their day's work for the railroad. They moved in unison, led by a very tall man in a black uniform. As he approached the door to the waiting room, I could see the silver whistle hanging from a cord about his neck. His stern, forbidding look kept us inside the waiting room. Our uncle directed us towards the far corner of the place where a silence, heavy with deep, dark secrets had settled. He left the door ajar so that we could hear the bell announcing the arrival of the train. No words were exchanged between my mother and my uncle as we waited. Their stiff, unflinching eyes chased away any need for conversation.

The cold, wet breeze filtering in through the door and blurring the glass with a thin line of vapor made me edge closer to my mother in search of warmth. A deep feeling of loss was taking possession of my chest; the tightness only grew deeper when the bell began to ring. I thought of all the contours of the road that led from the train station to the fountain in the main square. Noticing my discomfort, my mother whispered quietly into my ear. "Do not show any fear in the presence of your uncle."

I tried to control my trembling hands, which I hid inside my coat pockets. "If I could only get a glimpse of the chestnut trees above the station, I would be able to stop trembling," I thought. I had spent many a Sunday afternoon under those chestnut trees listening to Grandfather Zelmi as he spoke of his wanderings beyond the village.

"One day you will also feel the urge to leave Sheshi and traverse the long road as each of us has done." That morning, waiting for the train to appear, I was leaving behind the dying flame of our fireplace and the countless stories searching to enter a receptive ear.

"We should move to the platform," Uncle Karmel said abruptly as he took hold of our only suitcase. The bell outside now rang more insistently, reverberating through the last hues of the night. Six people in all were standing on the platform. An elderly couple at the other end huddled closely together and grasped a white sack knotted at the top. As I looked at them, the silhouette of the chestnut trees, together with their scent and the rustling of their leaves, made their way into the mirrors of my eyes. After so many years, they are still with me, as vigorous and memorable as on that early morning in 1959.

When the train emerged from the tunnel, the dawn almost dimmed its front light. The smoke it emitted filled the station with the smell of burned coal. Typical of the trains in this part of the country, it was an old locomotive and traveled as slowly as the people themselves, who were in no hurry to allow their lives to be dictated by precise machinery. "I will take care of your house and tend to your chestnut and olive trees," Uncle Karmel assured my mother in a steady voice. I had been expecting an emotional departure, but the fear of betraying any weakness abated with this uneventful separation.

When the doors to the wagon opened, I saw that the carriage was almost empty. Seated next to the window in order to see the lights at the far end of the village, watching out over the white adobe houses, I recalled Grandfather saying, "The lights in Sheshi look at each other as young lovers do when they see one another for the very first time. They pull you towards them and fill your heart with nostalgia. It is then that one realizes that he must come back to the village. That light will accompany you wherever you go." Grandfather had spoken the truth. But from the window of the train compartment I could only see the cemetery lights shining more brightly than any other.

The door closed and a piercing whistle surged from the locomotive. At the last gate to the station stood the tiny figure of Uncle Karmel, his shoulders curved as two dry twigs by the experience of the last war. He did not lift his arm to wave a last goodbye, even though I had imagined that the emptiness of the train station might have gotten the best of him. He simply disappeared into the undefined colors of the early morning, and that was the last time I saw him.

Years later, in our home across the ocean, I overheard my father reading a letter telling of Uncle Karmel's death to my mother. Uncle Karmel had died beneath a chestnut tree in the field above the train station. It must have been in late August, for the letter still smelled of lavender. The authorities of Sheshi had organized a massive search for the old war veteran when he had failed to appear at the ceremony at which he was to receive his twentieth medal of honor. They had found his body three days later in a pool of mud. Because the rains had fallen for two straight days, his corpse was nearly submerged, head down.

The letter explained in detail how Uncle Karmel's Great-Aunt-Alba had warned him not to go to the field, but rather to wash himself with water boiled with basil leaves. After hearing the dogs bark for nine days and nine nights, she had seen Uncle Karmel struggling against the waters of the brook down below the village. On that day, she had taken her final walk from her house to the bottom of the village, aided by two crutches made by her husband. "Your time has arrived," she had warned Karmel, to which he had replied, "You should have saved your strength for later days. If you could really read the stars, we could actually put things in order."

"I just wanted to have a clear conscience," Great-Aunt-Alba had replied. She had repeated these very words to the village authorities when they found his body later.

The trip back home had proven much more difficult for the woman. She had been obliged to watch for the stones and the stares of the people through their half-opened doors. Very few of them could recognize her, though, because, while she had aged just like everyone else had, she nonetheless retained a uniquely piercing, youthful look.

Great-Aunt-Alba had stopped at the fountain in the main square to wash her hands and to cool her forehead. It was then that she, and everyone else in the village, had heard Uncle Karmel's dog howling like a man in agony. "May he finally rest in peace in God's arms," the old woman had muttered as she quenched her thirst and washed her hands three times. Her family was fast disappearing from Sheshi. "One day," she thought, "not even our name will remain in the people's minds. They will have to go to the cemetery to learn of our existence."

The news of Uncle Karmel's death soon reached all of Sheshi and the neighboring villages. Tied to an apple tree, the dog had kept howling unbearably for two whole days. This in itself had been enough to convince the townspeople that Karmel was dead; after all, they had always seen the two together on every occasion and at every encounter. "Release the dog and he will lead you to Karmel's body," Great-Aunt Alba had advised after the two days of downpours had brought down rivers of mud into the village streets.

When the authorities had arrived at the scene of death, the dog already had licked so much of the mud from his owner that the men were astounded not only by the cleanliness of the body but also by the dark blue color of the skin. The dog, sitting with its feet crossed beside the cadaver, had seemed unmoved by the approaching throngs of people, who had been beckoned by the blue of the sky, which seemed to have descended upon the dead man. Nor did the dog stir when the corpse was lifted from the water and covered with the clear white sheet which the priest, certain that the dead blue face was a sign of the presence of the Almighty, had quickly blessed with holy water.

"God shows His presence in many ways," the priest told

the people who attended the funeral Mass. The casket was placed directly underneath the main altar, filled with every blue flower that the villagers could find. Years later, all those who had attended the rite could still remember the clear, sparkling voice of the priest as he sang the "Song of Songs." His words were accompanied by thousands of musical instruments that crowded the top of the dome, although no one could swear to having seen them.

"I heard the music just as everyone else present did," each would affirm for years to come, "but don't ask me where it came from. I heard it just as clearly as I now hear you speaking to me." Deep down, they all kept on hearing the strange, soothing music. It stayed with them for years, and mothers continued to pass it on to their unborn children. The one who could not forget even one note of that celestial harmony was the priest.

"We are going to call for another priest," declared the President of the Association of Christian Women for the Preservation of the Memory of the Grief of the Virgin Mary. It so happened that, since the event of the celestial sounds, the priest had paid little attention to the women's confessions on Friday afternoons, until the women sensed in themselves such a feeling of uncleanliness as to render them unfit to continue as members of the association, let alone to be near their husbands, for fear of further aggravating their precarious spiritual state of being.

Finally, the vicar of Melfi sent a young seminarian who had not yet taken his third vow. The vicar wanted to test the young man and to make certain that he had chosen the right path. The youth's blonde hair and rosy skin attracted all the young girls to Sunday Mass. The square filled with these young women, promenading up and down in their best outfits. The men sat on the café steps alongside the fountain, and when there was no space for all of them, they even climbed onto the fig tree to catch a glimpse of the girls. This time, it was the men who were unhappy with the situation. The women no longer had time to iron their shirts or to polish their shoes. The children were sent out into the street while their mothers prepared themselves for days before Sunday Mass. In a short time, the villagers assumed a strange look, and a deeply secretive atmosphere loomed over the rooftops of Sheshi. Each woman spent the early morning hours before her husband awoke embroidering her own dress.

As the women's desire for the young seminarian grew, a sense of estrangement settled over every home of the village. Husbands and wives would stumble upon one another in the square without so much as recognizing one another. "The young priest-to-be has cast a spell over our women," the men muttered as they sipped their coffee.

"There is only one way to bring them back," asserted the eldest of the group, who had rarely said anything in all the years he had spent at the café reading the same newspaper over and over again. Now yellowed and tattered, the first page held a photograph of a very tall building with a pointed spear. The rod on top of it seemed to catch the lightening which arched in a serpentine twist through the sky.

Amidst total secrecy, a few of the men in the café decided to turn the young seminarian into a night star. They consulted the oldest woman in the village, and she agreed to prepare a love potion made of ingredients that no one would be able to trace.

One morning in May of that year, the authorities hung up a public announcement of the seminarian's death on the front wall of the municipal building. Rumor had it that the young man had been asphyxiated by the first breeze of spring which had nestled in his room with all the floral scents it could muster. The women were taken by such sadness that for years to come they never wore a new dress, but walked in silence with their hair disheveled. At home at night, in spite of the door's being locked, screams and curses filtered up from the street below through the weather-beaten windows as my father read and reread the letter from Sheshi to figure out the real cause of the young seminarian's death.

"We now live in a land where mysteries are solved with mathematical precision and where any effect can be traced directly to its cause," he asserted with pride. So the letter was dissected even to its very last sound in order to discover a logical explanation for the death of the young priest in the village left behind. Week after week, Father sat next to the window that overlooked a little green area behind the tall apartment buildings where each tenant grew his own selection of vegetables; there, he followed the flight of the few black birds that glided above the patch of green.

Finally, Father wrote a long letter to the Mayor of Sheshi, making it known that he had come a little closer to solving the mystery. His desire to notarize precisely what had occurred to the seminarian became so overwhelming that he even deprived himself of the customary walk he took after the evening meal through the main avenue of the city up to his newly acquired barber shop. This shop had soon become the center for conversations in many languages. There the clients even took up the matter of solving the mystery of the young priest, but Father soon grew discouraged. Evidently, there were so many disputes over the many possible causes and effects that the clients were not communicating. Eventually, Father ceased altogether talking of the case. His walks to the barber shop lasted longer and longer.

To ascertain that the shop would still be there, visible to

all, Father left the swirling blue, white and red light in front of it on. He returned home when the streets became quite empty. Because the cars were parked along the curbs, the air was cleaner and the nights were instilled with silence. Nothing stirred but the remnants of strange voices high up in the tenement buildings.

"They are the unheard noises left behind by the people who used to sit on the steps of the building long ago, playing dominos or simply re-coloring the place with those of the old memories left behind." This was Mother's way of explaining the incomprehensible voices. She even declared that she could still make out their faces when she sat with them on the tenement stoop as a complete stranger. To her, the faces pitted together on those steps brought to mind the timeless space in the square of the old village where the flow of the waters from the fountain mirrored the flight of the swallows through the marine blue sky. I could see how burdensome it was becoming for her to maintain the details of the life left behind. Her distant expressions brought to mind her apparently unemotional detachment from Sheshi as the train moved slowly away from the station's platform.

That expression had become tinged with the colors of fear as we arrived at the city by the sea. It was very early in the morning, and the lights on the lampposts had just been extinguished. People entered and exited coffee shops in a great hurry as we followed the signs outside the train station to the special office set aside for people who needed medical clearance. I carried our only suitcase, secured in four places by white string, while my mother gripped my younger brother by the hand. A porter, a young man with shoes untied and worn half-through, accompanied us to the immigration office. He was no older than I, but he had the look of a very mature person. Certain and unperturbed, he moved briskly ahead of us, never turning to see if we were following. But, behind the fearsome expression, there was the look of a frightened and lonely being. This was the same sort of look that my older brother, Rini, had worn when he waved his hand to us as he stepped onto the train on his way north to work as an apprentice in a big barber shop. Rini had turned his head back as if he had forgotten something, and, as the train withdrew from the station, he was still waving a supplicant goodbye.

I remember taking Mother's hand as we entered the immigration office. It was as cold inside as the walls of our house in the village in the winter. The tightness I felt in my throat that early morning in the big city by the sea was to remain with me until the very end of my last memories.

"This is the place you are looking for," announced the young guide as he looked straight into our eyes. Over the door to the consulate perched a white-winged eagle with a shiny black beak. The floor was immaculate and altogether empty of furniture. Instead, a lengthy line of people, each grasping a pile of papers, leaned against the wall of the long corridor. Not a whisper was heard nor a gaze met among any of them as they bore up beneath a deep air of apprehension.

We were led into the reception room and asked to separate. My mother and younger brother were taken where the women lined up, whereas I was placed in a large room with men of all ages. One by one, we were lead into a shower room and given a number. Four doctors, whose only visible feature was the color of their eyes, examined and x-rayed us. A woman, whose white teeth seemed to float in the dark cavity of her mouth, handed us a number of geometric figures to arrange on a table. She counted from one to ten and quickly removed the box, whereupon we froze in the thick wall of silence. The fear of failing the medical examination (and thereby killing one's hopes of ever again seeing one's relatives in the lands beyond the seas) dominated that chamber. This was the place where dreams were made or unmade by a simple stroke of a pen on the papers that each one of us carried so carefully from desk to desk. No one knew what the papers contained.

At last, we were led before the person in charge of the final approval or rejection. Leaning over the documents, he mechanically scanned them beneath his black eyebrows. No words were exchanged. Whatever feelings could have existed ...and I am certain that they had to be there ...were utterly suppressed. It was then and there that I first sensed the coldness and the mantle of isolation that enveloped each official in the office of immigration. The grey of the endless corridor, undecorated by a picture of any kind, augmented the aura of indifference that followed us as we moved from one room to the next.

In the room where they finger-printed us, rolling one finger at a time on a paper with ten boxes, the clock marked one o'clock in the afternoon. Bigger and more imposing than any piece of furniture in that windowless room, its hands moving from line to line, the clock provided the only sound, albeit a distant ticking. We gasped for air.

There were nineteen other new arrivals of all ages. They looked different from the people I had seen in the main square of Sheshi, and their language, so diverse from person to person, did not sound like mine. I was discovering a world that I had not even known existed beyond the seven mountains. I remember feeling a strong urge to speak to the man next to me, a man with unusually large hands and curved fingers. But all I could manage was a far away smile to which I received no response. Among the man's apparent preoccupations, one loomed largest: to secure the stamp of approval on those carefully guarded documents.

From this place where I now come to sit in the late afternoons to watch the automobiles slip by, I remember that I never did manage to speak to any one of them. I would have liked to know where they were going and what places they were destined to reach. But perhaps, just as I could see no further than the gray walls in the corridor, neither could they.

I wondered how Mother was faring. More than five hours had passed since we had been separated. What weighed on everyone's mind was the possibility of being rejected, either for harboring an unknown disease or for failing to place those geometric figures into their proper spaces quickly enough. The humid afternoon that had slipped into the room from the corridor began to feel as heavy as the doctors' furtive looks as they passed in front of us while we moved from room to room. The crushing silence was only interrupted occasionally by the clacking of typewriter keys, the noise of which cut deeply into the bodies of those who, not daring to make a move for fear of doing something to disturb the order of things, stood immobile in their assigned place. The hands of the large clock on the wall moved implacably, with no apparent concern for the anxiety that the room was exhaling. For a while, I followed the movements from one second to the other, counting until my mind drifted away to the unfamiliar sounds of the sea waves as they slammed against the rocks of the seaport.

The morning of our arrival, the guide had walked ahead of us, turning around, at times, to give us a faintly discernible, distant smile, as if he wanted to say something but could not. Something kept him in an aura of isolation. Of course, the privacy of his demeanor only encouraged my mother's desire to get closer to him to discover the cause of the sadness that lodged in his eyes. Now I realized that the city that was known to write songs with the sounds of the waves was other than what those sounds concealed. A small puppet theatre in the neighborhood revealed its deep melancholy perhaps better than did the throngs of people buying and selling. In the small boutiques, the multicolored artifacts, gently shaped in so many different forms and painted in colors extracted from the surrounding countryside, contrasted sharply with the broken bottles and crumbled papers that littered the street.

The consulate building, with its marble entrance and gray shutters, was surrounded by a tall iron fence. Around it, countless people with deep blisters on their legs did not pay any heed to the stench that had settled upon them. It was then that I understood that the penetrating sadness in the guide's eyes was a kind of melancholy that went beyond the desire of the sea waves to snatch the colors of the countryside. The eternal imprint of misery and desolation upon the city that endured its pain silently while it made others sigh with love shattered the dreams of hordes of people who embarked for unknown lands. An intense heat had settled on the marble building like nets left to dry on the rocky beach that girded the city. The blue sea water, which quietly caressed the rocks with its foam, went unnoticed by the fishermen lacing together the broken nets. Small boats, collecting the sun's rays which arrowed the sea and spread upon it thousands of stars, sailed towards the horizon.

In the corridor of the building I sensed the imposing presence of nothingness and the impossibility of sharing a common existence with those present. By now, the smell of a wet wind had invaded the room where twenty of us had been left alone, each with documentation in hand and a number hanging from his neck. Some were younger than I was;

others were much older. I often thought of the impenetrable world that each of them hid and felt an urgent desire to get to know the events of their existence. The deep lines that crossed their foreheads testified to their age and sensitivity to the needs of others.

One clean-shaven man particularly attracted my attention because of the ceaseless twitch of his left eye and the cracking of his fingers. He appeared to be the eldest in our group. He remained throughout the whole ordeal as inscrutable as the measured looks and movements of the doctors who examined us. His fingers moved faster and faster as the clock ticked like a knife cleaning blood from an open wound. The image of the young guide leading us to the immigration building had slowly faded away as one of the doctors opened the door to our room. An array of eyes followed the creaking sound of the door as it topped the pangs from the heartbeats of the twenty of us.

I was given a second set of documents and told to line up on the right side of the room. The only one who remained behind as we were moved into another room across the long corridor was the old man with the wrinkles and the twitching fingers. I would gladly have switched places with him. I learned afterwards from the person standing in front of me and to whom I had addressed not a word, for he appeared cloaked in fear, that the old man had been rejected because he was suffering from trachoma. It was not the first time he had been rejected. He wanted to see his wife and children, who had crossed the wide ocean and traveled through many horizons to work in coal mines. "There," the person in front of me added, "anyone can work who is not afraid of the dark and the black dust that gnaws at your lungs with every breath that you take. He will try again soon with the hope that a kinder examiner will take pity on him. In the village they say that he gets the strength to go on living from the daily wait for the letter from the Immigration Office to be examined again."

From the window of the room I could see the tall, massive ship docked. Dozens of dockworkers moved the merchandise along wide concrete pavement just as so many little ants carrying away bits of leaves to store underground for the winter. The sun was setting far away where the waters met the sky coloring the surface with a rosy mist. I was still thinking of the old man who would not be taking the trip with us, but the others in the room had dispelled the gloomy look from their face and were looking at the sunset with its glow in their eyes. The promise of a new land with a new life and a secure future for their children, embedded in them by countless others who had traversed the same road before, had gotten the best of them. There was no argument that could dissolve those nurtured images in them. They knew precious little of the harsher life that awaited them and that would ultimately consume every vestige of humanity that they carried with them.

That evening I saw my mother with a faint smile on her lips. We were given a new number and a large yellow envelope with all the necessary documentation for embarkation. The line of people, with all the belongings they could carry, stretched for as far as the eyes could see. They looked like so many sheep descending from the barren hills to the village, leaving behind a burning sunset. The people, like the sheep, followed the scent of the cave where they could spend the night and hope to climb even higher the next day for greener pastures among the rocks.

My mother had said very little. She held my brother and me close to her as we waited for the signal to embark. The olive trees on the nearby hills sloped in terraces shone with thousands of silvery leaves beneath the last rays of the sun before plunging into the sea. From time to time, like white silhouettes, dots of peasants could be seen pulling their animals of burden by the bridle downhill towards the barely visible rooftops of the villages. The silence that reigned in the long lines of people waiting to see the gate to the side ladder of the ship open rendered almost audible the footsteps of the peasants descending from the hills.

I could sense the pounding of my mother's heart as she attempted to cover my younger brother with her mantle to protect him from the chilly breeze of the approaching night. The line was a procession of tiny figures clustered together to guard the few belongings tied to their back. With eyes downcast, they moved toward the tall ship with mountains of bright lights. They were attracted to it like fish to the moonlight. The city behind us was asleep; the few lights left on for the night were the only indication of a city in slumber. The ship's lights floated in the sky like so many stars searching for a cradle in the infinite darkness.

We were directed into cubby-hole number six hundred sixty-seven, more a crypt than a cabin, with three beds stacked one on top of the other. The middle-aged man who traveled with my brother and me was to get off at our first stop. He was filled with trepidation. "I am going to the heart of Africa to work in the gold mines," he said, his voice faltering at every syllable.

The ship sailed past midnight, leaving behind the lights fading into the darkness of the sky. Those were the last words I heard from our cabin mate. In the morning, just after the sun had reached its highest point in the sky, from the third-class passenger deck, I saw a small boat approach and then leave the ship, bearing one extra person. Although we had said nothing more, I presumed that he knew where my family was going. There was a tacit understanding among all the passengers not to be too inquisitive for fear of multiplying the uncertainties that each of us felt.

The small boat sailed away, partially hidden by the high waves. The fading image of the passenger, his collar turned up to protect himself from the wet wind, was quickly engulfed by the perfectly sustained rhythm of the rising and falling waters.

Soon after, it began to drizzle. At times the pungent raindrops turned into snow flakes, only to melt as they touched the surface of the deck. Red flags were placed on every door that led to the deck because of the approaching storm. They were expecting heavy winds. The young pressed against the windows of the enclosed deck space, watching the waves hurl against each other.

From the other side of the transparent wall sat the first-class passengers. The men were all dressed in black tuxedos. The women, with their long dresses and unusual hairdos, thin and pale, vented multicolored fans and drank from elongated glasses. The sound of music that seeped through the invisible divide brought to mind the organ music that made the paper angels come down from the vault of the main church in Sheshi on Christmas Eve. The figures behind the glass wall bent and straightened to the rhythm of the music, revealing only measured smiles and controlled hand movements. Beyond the enclosed deck, the thickening fog suffocated the feeble cries of the ship's lifeboats.

The crossing was to take ten days, but it soon became difficult to count them. The deck where the third-class passengers were permitted to linger for a bit of fresh air and a quick glimpse of the sky gradually emptied of people. The sickness and the smell that was caused by the choppy sailing spared no one. Dark grey clouds raced alongside the ship for days. At dusk, they could not be seen, but the deep, dark roar surging from the depths of the ocean told us that they were still with us.

At the corner of the enclosed deck, a passenger was seated with his legs crossed. He smoked nervously. An older person wearing a blue sailor hat approached the table carrying a chair which he had dragged from a nearby table. The two men seemed to know each other. The younger man quickly extinguished his cigarette and made room for the visitor, who removed his hat and placed it at the far edge of the table. Like the young man, he was dark with an aquiline nose and light eyes, illuminated ever more brightly by the light fixture shining over the table. Soon a paper was spread upon the table, but I could not decipher the writing. The waves beat furiously against the ship, which sailed, unperturbed, from wave to wave.

Both men looked about, as if expecting the arrival of someone else. I took another glimpse at the table and noticed a map spread over it with deep lines where it had been creased repeatedly. "This is where the city of Chicago is," announced the older man as he pointed to it. Many years later, that name was to become familiar to me. My presence, which had clearly become evident to both men by now, was of no concern to them. The older man pointed out to the other just where Chicago lay in relation to the city that was to be the port of entry for all of us. The younger person turned around and repositioned the map as he strove to visualize the place circled in pencil. "A man dressed in black will be waiting for us when we disembark. The train we will be taking, I was told in the village, moves as swiftly as a snake under a pile of hay. We will be at our destination in two days after our arrival at the port," added the older man, with conviction.

I learned days later on the ship that most of the men carried with them a signed contract to work in the meat-packing industry. Forty per cent of their salary would go to the agency which hired them for the duration of the contract. I got as close as I could to listen to their conversations. "I was told," said another of the group, "to put a cross at the bottom of the page where he held his finger, even though I could sign my own name."

I could see that each of them was trying to reassure the other while at the same time showing as much firmness as possible under the circumstances. "Chicago," he continued to say without being able to hide the fear in his eyes, "is a city that reaches further than the last horizon visible from the highest hilltop of the village. The place is lit with countless street lamps that stand as tall as our trees in the square, and the people, many a time, cannot distinguish between the day and the night. There is great abundance in that land that seems to float on top of a sea of green grass."

In silence, each man was reliving the day of departure and jealously guarding that invisible pack of dreams that was sustaining him in his voyage. Every now and then, the younger men in the group glanced at the ocean from the windows of the enclosed deck, even though they knew very well that it would reveal nothing. One of them could not resist the temptation to divulge what the man he shared his cabin with had said. "In Chicago there are places where men and women gather to drink. The women are dressed like the ones one sees in a magazine. There, they even bring drinks to you, and there is always enough money left to tip them." The dark chestnut eyes of the young men who listened to this tale shone even more brightly than the chandelier that hung above the enclosed deck.

But the older men with distinct olive-copper skin did

not seem to partake of that delight. In their minds were the wives and children they had left behind with only scant provisions that could last no more than six months. After that, they would be at the mercy of their relatives until their husbands and fathers could send some money. The letter from the consulate took from four to five years to arrive. Within it was the permission for families to rejoin their men in the new land. If complications should arise with the Immigration Office in Naples, the last resort was to leave everything up to God, with the intercession of the priest. And, indeed, it was not unusual for people in the villages, for reasons of human nature...be it envy, hatred or pure malice...to send anonymous letters to the Immigration Office denouncing those waiting to rejoin their husbands or brothers. When that happened, rejection followed without explanation. Dreams came suddenly to an end for many divided families. They spent the rest of their days in anger and distrust of everyone else in the village. Some even went so far as to take revenge on those whom they imagined had sent the anonymous letters. The fact was, however, that the secret remained a secret forever, while it consumed those afflicted by it and nurtured those who had perpetrated the act. This was the very thought that afflicted the older men in the group and kept them from sharing the pleasures, mentioned with such zeal by the younger ones, that awaited them in the new land.

The ship seemed to be swaying more than it had in the morning and, indeed, the sea had swelled to greater heights. Darkness had engulfed the enclosed deck. Three loud whistles summoned the passengers down to their cabins. The ship was completely at the mercy of the high waves which rushed with great force and precision against it. The waves hammered against the cabin's tiny window all night long.

I thought of the rainy days in Sheshi in the last days of November. It was the month to remember the dead. Mother had begun to knit a woolen scarf from chunks of sheep's wool, which she had turned into fine yarn. The heavy rain beating against the windowpane did not perturb her.

A few weeks before, she had celebrated the arrival and baptism of her youngest son with neighbors and relatives. A long wooden table had been set up on our street. It was covered with sliced whole wheat bread, aromatic green olives and dried black olives. Hard cheeses, aged during the previous year, stood next to smoked sausages and freshly-picked chestnuts. A wooden wine cask was placed at each end of the table. Mother was as happy and as proud as a young mother with her firstborn child as she cradled the baby, whose every article of white clothing she had stitched by hand. This was one of those days for celebration which brushed aside the pernicious travails of the villagers' daily lives in the fields. Even the sparrows dared to snatch some of the hay, set out in bales to dry, and spirit it stealthily up through the clouds of the approaching winter sky.

The crowd patiently awaited the arrival of the priest from the nearby mountain church to celebrate the baptism with the holy water brought from the monastery between the mountains of the two-headed eagles. A young man who had just come of age was sent to the highest hill of the village to announce the arrival of the holy man by ringing a copper bell. On that day, the priest had set out from the monastery before sunrise. He had decided to take the shorter route through the deep but shady ravine. He was determined to be on time for the ceremony and, thereby, to dispel his reputation for stopping at every tavern located at the nine crossroads that connected the monastery to Sheshi. But it was not to be.

This time, however, it was an encounter with a stranger that held the priest back as he hastened towards the village. That afternoon, the heat was exceptionally intense, as it had been, in fact, for the entire week. The cicadas had returned to rub their wings, and the ants had completely invaded the fruit-bearing trees, attracted by the irresistible sugar dripping from the pruned branches. This would in the end prove to be their last intoxication. A cold wave followed which froze them solid to the bark of the fruit trees.

"I was detained by the Devil," asserted the priest. "He took the form of a beautiful white owl and spoke in Latin, turning his head around with every word. He said the following, 'Nosce te ipsum, por memo me impune lacessit.'"

This phrase angered the people even more, for their inability to understand it convinced them that they were being made fools of by the priest. So shaken was the priest by the encounter, for which he had been waiting ever since the day he had taken his vows for the priesthood, that he could have sworn to his superior that the owl itself forced his hand to tremble as he poured the holy water over the child's head. Yet, he felt overjoyed that he was able to fight off that temptation; even more, he believed that the encounter proved his dedication to the church had not been in vain, for the Devil really did exist.

That was the last time the people in the village saw the priest sober, even though he had refused every effort by the guests to have him taste their special wine. He had seemed strangely at peace with himself, smiling with the candor of a young child to everyone who acknowledged him. The last person to see him leave the village, oddly enough by a road that went all around the village only to end at the same place it began, was old Viti.

"The priest never came back after the second time around. I waited for him to come back for the third time, but he never did. The sun had already settled below the lowest of the seven mountains, turning the sky into a red cauldron." Old Viti was to relate this tale for the rest of his life as he sat among the others on the wooden bench of the main square watching the swallows silhouetted between the sky and the water basin of the fountain.

"Your younger brother is God's creation," Mother always reminded me as she set aside the last piece of hard bread for him. She would soak the bread in water, chew it and then place tiny pieces of it in his mouth. "The celebration of your own baptism went well into the night," she said to me with her usual look of pride. "You were the biggest baby the village had ever seen, so we baptized you just a few hours after your birth. The priest was afraid that God would call you back to your place in Heaven because of your round, rosy face, your high cheekbones, and your light hair."

The day that Father departed from Sheshi...a day that seems so long ago at this very moment...he told Mother to keep his children close to her skirt. At the same time, he asked me to keep a close eye on our house. Neither Mother nor Father shed a tear. The train emerged crowned with the black smoke from the tunnel. The passengers climbed the steps to the carriage and the train quickly departed, as if it wished not to prolong the pain of separation.

The only person who showed any emotion was the stationmaster, who took out his checkered handkerchief and pretended to wipe the dust from his eyes. Much later, I learned that he and Father had sat next to each other on the first day of school in one of the rooms of the richest family of Sheshi. The schoolroom was and remained for many years the only one in the village. The trainmaster, whose name everyone in the village had heard but no one could remember, kept a list of all those who left the train station for the distant lands across the ocean. The long list included the day, the hour, and the family name. The only thing that was missing was the final destination of each passenger. Years after his retirement, it took months for the stationmaster to read the names of those who had left the village to the curious ones at the café. Many of the young wanted to know the names of the family members, what they looked like, and whether they would ever come back to the village. "If you want to know their faces, go to the cemetery. There the faces are cloaked forever from the effects of the cold and the heat."

As the years went by and blindness seized the trainmaster, the need to recall the moments of the silent goodbyes at the train station became the main weapon in the struggle against forgetfulness. The children of Sheshi thought of him as the blind old man with a black cap who read from a long list of names, at times only to a few people, but mostly to himself.

One clear morning in early April, with the sky filled with thousands of swallows, the owner of the café found the trainmaster still seated in front with his arms crossed and a streak of blood hardened by the cold mountain breeze. He had died from a stone thrown by a group of children who made fun of his unstoppable mumbling. It was never discovered who had thrown the fatal rock, and since no one came forward, the authorities closed the case. But they forbade the children from ever again playing in the square of the main fountain and from lighting a candle at the tomb of the trainmaster for the rest of their days.

For the old men of the village, who occupied the wooden bench across from the fountain in the square, this was a bad decision. The children's presence in the square brought them back memories and filled their eyes with pleasant reveries that blurred the passing of time and loosened the pain which gripped their joints. "Sad times will make their home in the village," commented the oldest, whose wrinkled eyes left no doubt of his age.

"The authorities, protected by their secluded offices and the machines that puff air from their bellies, have been given too much power by the officials of the big city beyond the seven mountains," added a second elder with conviction. All together, the elders decided to no longer follow the movement of the clouds that foretold rain, nor the patches on the moon at its fullest stage that told them when to plant the seeds.

The eager young peasants and the municipal officials were at a loss as to how to remedy this very peculiar situation. They consulted with the higher office of the big city and with all the almanacs they could find around a wide perimeter of the seven mountains. To their astonishment, they found out after months of research that they could not read beyond the scribbling on the page. The tiny symbols in black and red ink were more like numbers which multiplied on the page as they jumped from one square to another. They soon realized that it was impossible to learn from the symbols when to turn the earth and seed it or how long a wait there should be before the harvest. What was even more troubling was the realization that the elderly, who never missed a day on the bench facing the fountain, were nowhere to be found. The officials blamed one another for their lack of attention to their grandparents and for not knowing their hiding place. The mayor mobilized the whole village. Every able-bodied man and woman was promised the best seat at the center of the stage during the grape harvest festival if they could retrace the steps of the elders and report their findings to the municipality.

To no one did it occur to consult the children of Sheshi, for neither the priest nor the mayor was aware of the invisible link (made up of all the spider webs the young could find at the entrance to the sacred cave, which many still said the village sprouted like a flower) that tied them to the memories of the elders. Sheshi had become a desolate place since the day of the decree that punished the children.

With the approaching days of winter, the women were convinced that the village was living its last days. On their own and in the utmost secrecy many of them had begun to make lifelong vows to the village's ancestors in the cave at the bottom of the ravine. By now, the constant dripping of water from the ceiling and the unbearable humidity had infested the sacred chamber with bats with long black wings. From the center of the ceiling, only the outstretched hands of Saint Leonard, with their white nails and terra cotta colored fingers, were visible. The younger ones at the threshold of womanhood flogged themselves until their chests bled with rivers of blood that lessened the pain that consumed their bodies from the inside during the hours of the night.

Sheshi was covered by dark clouds that rained down drops of sadness in the early morning hours. The people who lived outside the only road that led to the main square of Sheshi would remember for years the smell of sorrow that spiraled up from the chimneys of the homes and made its way down to the sacred cave. For a long time, the entire village remained isolated with no one being able to enter and no one able to leave. The people of Sheshi became estranged from one another; secretly, they blamed each other for the disease that was afflicting each of them.

Only the forced resignation of the whole executive

committee and the coming snows persuaded the elderly and the children, after long discussions on the banks of the winding brook, to decide to start the journey back to the main square of the village early the next day. To accompany them, the oldest of the elders summoned all the snails around the edge of the brook to bend the tall grass and prepare the way for their return to the village. The children gathered all the berries they could hold in their hands and fed them to the swallows as they whirled around and in front of the caravan.

The first to notice the return of the birds was the white-bearded shepherd who tended his flock on the hidden side of the mouth of the brook. There, the waters were cooler and the grass, taller. He cherished this secret with his watchdog, who first led him to the lush greensward. Now the dog barked and ran from beneath the legs of the sheep, waking the shepherd from his slumber under the mulberry tree. The shepherd saw no need to send the dog to inform the villagers.

The ringing of all the bells in all the churches of Sheshi filled the sky with thousands of swallows. The birds swirled around the bell towers, catching as many of the sounds as they could. The joyous occasion snatched away from the villagers the veil of sadness that had descended and remained over their eyes for many months. Life in the village slowly came back, and with it, memories of a not too faraway past. The women hung their best embroidered canopies out of their windows or over their balconies. Never had Sheshi seen so many different designs and colors adorning the front walls of the homes. The almond trees were dusted and carefully pruned before the first breezes arrived from Africa. The door to the Church of the Dead was left open for thirty-three days and nights. The twelve saints who lined the knave of the church were garlanded with home-grown flowers, the first violets of the year. The ousted members of the municipality were made to not only clean the wooden bench where the elderly had sat before their departure from the village but also to add to it a leg-stretcher for their tired limbs.

At midday everyone gathered at the crossroads between the cemetery and the sacred cave to await the arrival of the caravan of the very old and the very young. The clock on the tower of the municipal building struck twelve times with unusual clarity. Years later it was said that the sounds had even pierced each of the seven mountains.

At the Church of the Blessed Mother, the priest found himself all alone praying at the mid-point between the day and the coming of the night. Prefti Vlasë did not mind that at all. It gave him the chance to be alone with the crucifix behind the altar, where he swore he saw drops of blood oozing from the wound of the Savior. He only mentioned the occurrence to his sister, who, while much older than he, had been his companion and confidante since she had found him. The return of the elders from their hiding place freed Prefti Vlasë from the agony of being unable to help the villagers with their planting and from the burden of providing them with answers as to why they had disappeared in the first place. His many prayers and supplications to the crucifix had not supplied him with a logical answer. The joy of the people of Sheshi became Prefti Vlasë's joy, for a heavy weight had been lifted from his shoulders. So, the day of the returning caravan found the priest kneeling in front of the main altar. He heard every sound from every corner of the village.

Prefti Vlasë had always possessed those strange powers that allowed him to descend through the infinite layers of sound. He had never shared his secret with anyone. Only his mother was aware of it, and the knowledge brought much apprehension to her. One winter evening she attempted to reveal her son's powers to her husband. "Your son," she told him as she added the last stitches to his last pair of socks, "can hear what no one else can and can see inside of things."

Her husband did not at first totally grasp what she was saying. "What do you mean, he can see inside of things?"

"He knows the way to the people's heart," she replied.

That revelation filled his father with an uneasiness that from that moment on prevented him from looking straight into his son's eyes. Prefti Vlasë's father had never been a religious person and there was no place for the Church in his circle of friends. That winter night he responded to his wife's confidence with nothing more than a shrug of the shoulders and the dry sound of an uncaring voice. It was another side she had never seen of her husband. Now he remonstrated, in the voice of a total stranger, "It is all in your mind and in those fables you have filled your mind with."

Yet, deep down, he knew that his son had a special sense. He could see it in the ways he identified objects and in the detailed perception he gave of what they held inside of them. This suspicion was verified when he saw a throng of butterflies weaving a garland around his son's head and spreading a pungent odor that kept the house smelling of spiders' eggs for days. Of course, he related nothing to his wife; but, from that moment on, he did nothing to interfere with his son's desire to share Jesus' agonizing hours on the cross and to share those feelings with anyone who touched his hands.

Soon after, the beginning of stigmata appeared on the palm of Vlasë's right hand. That is how, at just ten years of age, he was taken to a monastery on the other side of the seven mountains by his father and mother. The trip by mule took two days. There, after a long climb by foot in the early hours of dawn, they came upon a massive gray structure that perched on the tallest mountain. Its walls and high towers were reflected clearly in the volcanic lake far below. A rope was sent down from the lower section of the monastery to bring up the new novice. A loud voice from the hill behind the left tower ordered the mother not to come any closer and to veil her face. The mother felt as if she were being stripped of her most precious possession. The young novice felt a deep urge to embrace his mother and to tell her that she would always be with him along with God.

For that temptation alone he was placed in a solitary cell. The isolation lasted for a complete cycle of the moon. Three times a day he was served a slice of bread and a glass of water. The monk designated to watch over him opened the eye on the door of the cell three times daily. The novice tested his will on the first day of confinement. His closeness to God helped him to overcome the few remaining memories of his family. The blind friar assigned to lead him along the path of light lessened the gentle pain of the uncertainties.

Vlasë's perceptive powers were revealed to his superiors one hot summer day as he and his mentor were seen going through the mount of rocks to set free a gush of much-needed water. From that day forward, the Abbot of the monastery took him under his wing, ordering his monastic cell to be filled with the sacred books of the library. Indeed, the abbot was convinced that Vlasë could show the others the entrance into the Aleph, that mother of all sounds. The once-blind mentor urged Vlasë to reveal to no one the fact that his sight had been restored; he wanted to search for God from inside the beauty of a flower. In fact, the mentor came so close to the young novice that the other friars had difficulties in distinguishing one from the other, either by sound or by scent.

Since Vlasë's arrival, the monastery had become a reservoir of grains and dried fruits. Whatever the young novice touched simply multiplied three-fold. It did not take long before the peasants living in the valley below noticed the constant smoke from the three chimneys of the monastery and the increased height of the grain silo. The news that vast stores of grain existed in the monastery spread quickly to all the forgotten villages of the area. Soon the friars in charge of provisions were subject to men of all ages and colors who constantly knocked at their door. Following the silent prayers and the daily meeting, every friar participated in a vigil to discuss the ever-increasing number of people coming to beg for food. The young novice was asked to use his special powers to increase the yield of wheat and potatoes.

The demand was impossible to meet. Worse still was Vlasë's realization that his powers were actually waning. Distressed, the future priest was now convinced that he was living in sin. His will to control both his power and his pride had been tested; unaware, he had fallen prey to them. In their place he now felt the fear of losing God's grace.

It was at this time, exactly eleven years and three days after his arrival at the monastery, that his mentor advised him to gather his few belongings and leave the premises by the left side of the wall adjacent to the chapel. The night, Prefti Vlasë remembered, had been moonless. A terrifying silence fell from the sky with the large snowflakes. He was given a Bible and was told, after a brief embrace, to read it nine times a day and to seek God's forgiveness for his arrogance ninety-nine times daily. The door shut quickly behind him. The deep urge he felt to turn around and wave his hand at his mentor died with him years later in the deep freeze of winter under a white mantel of silence. And now, as he prayed in front of the bleeding crucifix, he was to realize that his failure to see the changes had been his punishment. Prefti Vlasë was destined to live his life in isolation until his sister, after years of searching for him, was able to rescue him from his loneliness.

In a dream as clear as the sky on a sunny winter's day, her mother had spoken to her. "Go to your brother and look after him. He is in need of us. Stay with him until God summons both of you." The next day, without telling anyone else of her dream, she took her old boots, her father's umbrella, and a hard piece of bread and began the search.

It was only after many more winters that a group of wandering Albanians searching for the land of the two-headed eagle was able to help her find the crooked bell tower where her brother served as a priest. "He knows you are coming," the eldest of the Albanians assured her. "He is reminded of your arrival every night, but he has grown old and may not recognize you at first. Do not be disheartened. He will know in due time that you are his sister."

And that is how she reached the village on top of a steep ravine barely visible from the small church of the crooked bell tower. The elderly Albanian with the half moon-shaped white hat took leave of Prefti Vlasë's sister with nothing more than a piercing look into her eyes. "We will have to cross the narrow sea to get to the land of our forefathers before the cold winds climb over the Carpathian Mountains. This is the place where you will be stopping." A fierce wind from the deep crevices of the ravine prevented her from hearing his words clearly, but she did note from him the kindest smile. It recalled to her the smile she had seen in her mother's coffin as she had placed on her the bouquet of white roses.

The caravan of Albanians vanished amidst the dust raised

by the carriages. She walked towards the front entrance of the chapel and asked the old man leaning with both hands on his cane which road to take to reach the village on top of the ravine. He lifted his gray-veiled eyes and, only after seeing her resemblance to Prefti Vlasë, did he tell her to take the road to the left where the pomegranate trees grow. "Do not take the one where the old cypress points to the sky," he admonished. "It will take you to the cemetery that lies between the olive groves." In the distance she could make out both of the trees; they seemed to be very close to one another, as lonely as the parched land surrounding them, and they were buffeted forcibly by the wind. It was a wind which appeared to bother the old man, standing with his eyes closed, no more than the arrival of a stranger had.

From the hilltop, Prefti Vlasë's sister could see the entire village. Sheshi stretched lazily from the lower ridge to the foot of the tallest of the seven mountains. In the middle, the main church, with its round bell tower, swelled like the belly of a sheep, dividing the village into two parts. Below the rows of houses, dozens of caves carved into the volcanic ridge displayed their chimneys, which sprouted directly from the earth like so many minarets. On the left of the road, just below the pomegranate grove, she noticed a small cave turned into a chapel. In its depths stood a small altar with three wooden crucifixes in a dark color. Across from the cave there was a wide rectangular wash basin, where two women in head scarves did their wash in silence.

It was a hot, sticky afternoon. The few dry shrubs that painted the scenery appeared to be suspended in the air. The only sound was that of the cicadas who inhabited a lone almond tree that stood agelessly amidst the dry grass. For a moment Angelina ... for that was Prefti Vlasë's sister's name ...was filled with doubt. "I wonder if he is going to recognize the same blood that flows through our veins," she pondered. In the old days the people would put all their trust in blood when it came to settling disputes. She remembered her father saying that blood had its own way of setting things straight. Little did Angelina know that Prefti Vlasë had known for years that she would come; he had spent every afternoon sitting on his balcony that overlooked the pomegranate grove just above the Chapel of the Virgin of Constantinople. "One of these days she will come;" this was the mantra he repeated to himself day after day when he closed the door to the balcony for the evening.

Prefti Vlasë knew everyone's footsteps and gestures from afar. On the afternoon of Angelina's arrival, however, he had succumbed to the desire he had felt all day to take a rest. Since the early hours of the afternoon, he had struggled to keep his eyes open. He had tried to dispel this persistent drowsiness by having more than the usual cup of black tea, but this ploy had worked for no more than a few hours. He had decided against a third cup, though, convinced that it was no use to delay what his body was naturally demanding. So, when Angelina arrived at the steps of the main church of Sheshi, unseen by anyone, her brother was fast asleep. It was one of those rare moments when his mind was completely blocked out.

Angelina banged the bronze lion's head against the metal button on the door and waited to catch her breath. The moment she had waited so long for had finally arrived. She could feel her mother's happiness inside of her, just as she had always felt it as a little girl. Prefti Vlasë awoke after the third knock. Upon opening his eyes, he knew that his sister's journey had come to an end. He descended the stone steps with a smile he could not hide. "Finally," he thought, "I will have company for the coming winter months."

He turned the door handle, trying to avoid its usual screech, and was for a second confused as to whether it was the mother or the sister who stood before him. "I have come to take care of you," she said in a suffocating voice as she tried to control her tears. She had been born during the first year of his novitiate. He now recalled the picture of his mother he had guarded in his mind for so many years. "I have prepared some tea," was all that he could manage as they tearfully climbed the steps toward the balcony. Prefti Vlasë felt a deep void inside of him thinking how much his sister had aged and how much clearer his memories of the past had been when the friars would sit all together in the cloister of the monastery waiting for the sun to set and to spread its rosy colors into the sky.

The last letter my father received from the village described in detail the profound changes that his sister's arrival brought to Prefti Vlasë. "The priest has not celebrated Sunday Mass since his sister, Angelina, arrived in Sheshi," my father whispered to my mother. From my study, which opened onto the kitchen, I could hear every sound. "The village should proclaim Prefti Vlasë a saint for all he has done to keep the memory of God alive," my mother insisted. Years later, when I entered my mother's world of memories, I learned what really had happened to Prefti Vlasë.

I recall it was the month of the deep freeze which followed weeks of one snowstorm after another. During one of those storms I was forced to spend the night and most of the next day at the house of one of our relatives. As I sat in his study, enclosed by a bookcase and by a long rectangular writing desk, I was given a letter to read which Doni, a distant cousin on my mother's side, had received some time ago.

"Now that you are here," Doni said, "I would appreciate

it if you could read this letter for me. I know it is not from my sister, for I do not recognize the scribbling on the page."

Doni knew each book by the color of the print and the design on its cover. It had been his life-long desire to learn how to read and write; in his old age, he had convinced himself that he would accomplish his goal. He had spent years looking for and buying books unique for their cover design. For that reason, the collection he had amassed followed no straight line of thought or discipline. Among them were a fine group of classics that I enjoyed leafing through to relive the magic of the written word.

Doni's books were his greatest prize. He would dust each one daily before he sat down to his cup of hot tea and lemon. That morning, through the partially unfrozen window, I could see a clear white sky. The snow sparkled as the sun's rays hit upon the tall banks lumped by the strong winds of the previous night. The world outside the window stood still, encroached only by an occasional flight of a few seagulls that had wandered in from the nearby ocean. Doni handed me the envelope and added, "I have a feeling there is some bad news written there. I have been dreaming of my sister ever since the postman hand delivered this letter to me. I could even see a distant sadness in his eyes that barely prevented him from saying something to me."

And, indeed, the bad news was enclosed within the very first sentence. "It fills me with sadness to have to tell you that your sister Emira has gone to join your mother and father." I did not know how to break the news to Doni, but he was able to read it anyway in my hesitation and in my eyes. I went on to the next sentence. "You should be happy, for Emira died on the same day that our priest, Prefti Vlasë, departed from this world with the light of God circling his head. It is believed that your sister was taken to Paradise by

Prefti Vlasë."

In an instant, silence settled into every empty space in the room. "She has been the umbilical cord for me," Doni muttered. "She brought our village into my house with every letter she sent." And then he admonished, "In this land, you must keep your mind filled with the memories of the past, for there is nothing in the present and total oblivion awaits the future." Years later I was to recall those very words while the hours of the day searched incessantly for the distant horizon.

I left Doni's home without saying a word. He had returned to dusting his books anew. In the streets, people were moving from place to place intent upon not touching or even coming close to any one of the other pedestrians. Any mishap was quickly followed by an automatic apology, which was taken as a deserved indemnity for the person's having suffered a violation of his private space. I thought of the miracle, mentioned in the letter,that had occurred during the funeral procession for Prefti Vlasë.

"The main square, where the fountain brings the cold water from the seven mountains, was filled with people from as far away as the two blue lakes with the mirroring image of the monastery. The children of Sheshi were all dressed in white like so many angels, and each one carried a white rose. A caravan of priests in black robes spread incense, filling the air with the smell of charred chestnut wood. As the procession reached the crossroad that cuts the village into four sections, a divine event took place. There was not a person in Sheshi who did not see Prefti Vlasë being lifted from the coffin and carried towards the setting sun by two fiery angels sowing stars. For days people prayed at the place where the miracle had occurred. More than a dozen people were trampled trying to touch the coffin where the body of

Prefti Vlasë had been positioned for three days and three nights. The pillow, embroidered by the women of the village and placed beneath his head, was installed on the altar of the main church and was declared a relic by the Bishop of Melfi. In the confusion that lasted for nine days and that had caused uncontrollable convulsions in many of those present, they forgot to bury your sister. It was only when the people began to smell the decomposing body and saw the almond trees in the square attacked by white worms that orders were given to bury the body deeper than usual in the family plot of the cemetery."

Chapter Six

I had left Doni shrouded in silence. The news that his sister had not received a proper burial at the proper time hardened his resolve to burn all the letters he had ever received from Sheshi. I had left him seated at the window with his eyes fixed on the falling snow. The snowflakes shone even more brightly against the deep darkness of the sky. Nothing could be heard but the softening layers of snow taking their place on top of one another.

From the end of the avenue I saw the light in our apartment building. It seemed to vanish in the distance with every step that I took. "I left the light on to guide you home," said my mother as she opened the door. I told her of the news Doni had received from the village. "I knew of Prefti Vlasë's death and that of Doni's sister for a while," she announced with a tone as indifferent as the darkness of the sky to the whiteness of the snow. "I have been dreaming of both of them for months," she added. "I even told your father, who dismissed the dreams with his usual comment. 'If everyone believed in your dreams, time would move backwards and we would all suffer from boredom.'"

That was during the longest winter in memory. It kept people home for weeks. I struggled to keep alive the sound of the elevated train as it approached the avenue near the pier where the tall ships with their round windows waited for the weather to break so that they could sail on. Every family in the neighborhood had taken refuge in their subterranean cell, and I wondered if they, as we, were rescuing their memories floating on top of the snowflakes.

My mother lived in our new home as if she had never left Sheshi. Her gestures and expressions were deeply embedded in the place whereshe had been born. But time spares no one. As one winter replaced another, growing only in ferocity, I saw the vanishing of world and the coming of the new one like a storm in the midst of summer. The change ravaged and spread the plague of the loss of memory without recognizable traces.

Our apartment was like all the others in the building. The only distinctions were the numerals attached to the door and the number of stairs dividing the five floors. One corridor always led into another ever narrower corridor. The families who dwelled in the apartments were rarely seen. Each took great care to lessen the noise before opening their door in the morning and closing it behind them upon returning at night. No one even attempted to know the neighbors living on the same floor.

And so the days and weeks came and went like all the rest. We had waited four and one-half years to be all together as a family; yet, the only day that happened was Sunday. The long separation from our father and our older siblings---a separation which would leave its mark on each of us---was now replaced by rigid hours of work with very little time to spare. This schedule forced the family members to be attuned to their own clock.

Mother was growing ever more taciturn by the day. We all knew what ailed her, but no one dared to bring it into the open for fear of shattering the feeble economic security that had been achieved. The obscure ailment that would not allow her to forget the village and her relatives was slowly consuming her. The traces of the malady could be seen in the wrinkles clustered about her grayish eyes; her ever present expression of sadness made it clear that she was totally removed from the objects which adorned the apartment. An invisible exile had begun for her. I knew that it was going to grow like a monster, and that it would devour all those who attempted to decipher the causes of its cancerous growth.

Winter gave way to a month of heavy rains. The streets turned into rushing rivers during the day and sheets of ice at night. Strong winds followed, eradicating the weakest trees that lined the avenues. From the front window of the apartment, I caught sight of the few blurred images of people daring to look out of their own windows. I thought of the swallows in Sheshi, swirling relentlessly around a lone rain cloud, trying to catch a few drops of water. Here a marked desolation crowned the pigeons clinging in clusters along the electrical wires connecting one tenement building to another.

In the Jewish grocery store across the street, they had just turned off the lights. In just a few months, the lights would go out permanently, once the grocer realized that not even the experience of the concentration camp, still present in the serial numbers on his right arm, was sufficient to fortify him against the street gangs which were proliferating. One such group, whose members were known for the blue tattoos along their own arms, repeatedly held up the store in broad daylight. The assaults, accompanied by the brandishing of bats and iron chains, had become such a ritual that the authorities were at a loss as to what to do. So, on a clear spring day just before sunset, the man with the black beard and the blue numerals on his right arm locked the door to his grocery store and, without looking back, never returned to the neighborhood. A few weeks later, I overheard two of the tenants in our own building mentioning that the owner of the grocery store had suffered a stroke that left him paralyzed and unable to speak.

I had watched that grocery store for hours while waiting for my father to return from his barber shop. Looking at the elderly couple in the grocery store going about arranging their produce in the morning and storing it again in the late hours of the day, I thought of the artisans in Sheshi with their workbenches outside their stores. The Jewish couple had seemed ageless. They seemed to have come from a place no one could locate on any map of the world. Their gestures and their habits seemed unlike those of all the people who entered and then left their store.

Different groups of people came and went from the neighborhood. Most of them left quickly, taking the unique colors and images that had been visible through the windows of their apartments. Others remained only to undertake the struggle of preserving the changes which they themselves had brought. Somehow, the Jewish couple had appeared to be above all of these constant changes, even as they gave the impression of having something of each of the diverse groups that inhabited the neighborhood.

The closing of the grocery store did not seem to be of much consequence to many of the neighbors. Indeed, it was not long before it was replaced by another, easily identifiable by the exotic fruits and the medicinal herbs that the new arrivals used as incense in their religious rites. This time, however, there was only one clientele. The customers spoke a language that was easily turned into music. Soon enough, the neighborhood was filled with notes from heretofore unfamiliar instruments. The old-timers packed their belongings by day and made their way out of the neighborhood by night.

Our home became as quiet as the midday hour. It was then that Mother began to draw the shades of all the windows facing the street. Life outside quickened; the traffic on the avenue increased in volume and speed. People rushed about as if they were about to miss a train at any moment. This fast new rhythm was meticulously organized and controlled by

176

an invisible hierarchy that ruled from inside the workplace; it gave people no chance to develop roots of commonality with each other. Our home, much as that of every other family, became an enclosed compound with insurmountable walls that kept everything alien outside.

The conversations which my mother and father shared over a cup of black coffee after dinner suddenly came to an end. My older brother and sister, whom we had not seen for four years and nine months, had grown estranged from the village. We were all clearly drifting apart.

My sister, who had not yet come of age when she left Sheshi with my father and older brother, had put aside the woolen doll she herself had made. Now she played with it only when she was alone in the apartment. She sat mending the winter clothes next to the window overlooking the street. The day after disembarking, she had gone to work as a seamstress with my aunt. She had learned the trade as a young girl in Sheshi, just as her ancestors had done for generations. Awakened by my mother daily just before the crack of dawn, she prepared lunch for everyone else with her eyes half closed. Then, with darkness still hovering over the tree tops, she went out to meet my aunt.

I remember my aunt's reminding my father about the child labor laws. "She is too young to work with older people," she scolded. And although he would reply, "They cannot tell her age because she is too mature and a good seamstress," my father was secretly trying to save as much as he could to take the whole family back to Sheshi. He did not want to offend his older sister, who had sponsored our immigration with her life's savings.

It was not long before we all became aware of Mother's deep sadness. She tried to hide it by keeping busy with all kinds of chores, which, at times, she would undo just to have something to do. But she could not contain a furtive smile when the monthly letter arrived from the village. She struggled against the inexorable passing of time that was sapping her strength and building distances between herself and her children. One night, as they took their usual places by the window facing the back of the building, Mother told Father, "One of these days we are going to be left alone. You are too busy with the barber shop to notice how fast our children are growing and how distanced they are becoming from one another."

My father's answer belied the depth of his own anguish. "A home is made to prepare others to make their own. It is best that you make peace with that and help them to learn to build." This was just the kind of reply that my mother dreaded to hear, but she did not argue. She had been taught never to contradict anything that her husband might say. She knew the fine line she was meant to walk. It had been handed down by her mother and inculcated even more forcibly by her grandmother, whose wisdom was nowhere in evidence in her own daughter.

Two winters had gone by since our arrival in the city. I had discovered the magic of books and the power of the written word, albeit in a new language. The entrancing beings who lived among those pages finally became my companions in the struggle against the deep loneliness and alienation I had begun to experience. With their help, the world outside our apartment felt less threatening, and the geometric designs I saw in the architecture, where my clouded eyes sought a place to rest and a point of contact, were slowly revealing their inner feelings. I sensed a ravaging silence emanating from the walls of the tenement buildings. I knew that, with time, it would only grow thicker, eventually depriving me of the space necessary to breathe.

I began to yearn for the arrival of the evening hours when everyone gathered around the dinner table at home. I noticed that the hour had become that time of the day that everyone in the family desired to witness, even though they never said so aloud. After five years of working in the sweatshop, my sister met the one with whom she was to spend the rest of her life. From that moment on, she rarely sat with the rest of the family at the dinner table. She spent the remaining hours of the day sitting and mending close to the window overlooking the street. She took her place there at six o'clock every evening and only left it when the darkness would prevent her catching a glimpse of the person who had entered her life.

My mother had become aware of the scar her feelings were opening in her demeanor even before she had taken up her perch at the window, but she made no attempt to thwart her daughter's passions. Having entrusted her with the responsibility of caring for my father and older brother when she was just twelve years old, my mother realized that the awful separation had confused her daughter's sense of childhood irrevocably. Indeed, my sister continued to make woolen dolls until late in her life, when she ran out of places to hide them. My mother's admonition to her served no purpose. "The day you decide to bring home this young man will also be the day that you get rid of your woolen dolls." I do not recall my sister's ever giving an answer. After clearing the table and putting away the dishes, she ran straight to the window, which by now was filled with boxes of red rose petals.

Even today, with my eyes as cloudy as winter skies, I can still smell the scent from those rose petals that brought to the window all kinds of birds from faraway places. Some of the birds, attracted by the floral aroma and deceived by the thick fog that descended into the street in early fall, crashed to their death through the windowpane. It happened in the early days of fall when the leaves of the trees lining the street confused them, throwing them off course from their route to warmer places. One morning Mother found the room filled with dead birds. She took it as a bad omen. She urged my sister to wear a collar of fresh garlic cloves and to stop looking out of the window. "Make certain you have all the pieces to complete your dowry instead of wasting your youth building wells of passions," she told her daughter one day as she was about to take her customary seat.

The only time my sister could be persuaded to leave her post was the hour of my father's return. Pulling down the shade the minute she saw the bus turn onto our street, she would join us at the dinner table, clinging to Mother as a chick to a hen. But when dinner was followed by the usual conversation that recounted the events of the day and the news from Sheshi, my sister would move her fingers nervously beneath the table. Pretending to follow the conversation, she would allow her eyes to settle anxiously on the window sill. In the reflection of the sun, slowly fading away, I saw rose petals weave a bridge between the window and the shining mirrors of her eyes. Her cheeks, dipped in the colors of the sunset, radiated the glow of a smile barely visible on her lips. Beneath the window of the apartment, leaning against the lamppost, stood the humble figure of her future husband gathering the messages as they made their way along the bridge of red petals.

My father came and went from the barber shop with the ebb and flow of the seasons. He never saw the figure leaning patiently against the lamppost unaware of the changes in the sky. But my mother was happy to see in her daughter the same hidden powers she had witnessed in her own grandmother as a child. On a spring day, with the park on the next street carpeted in violets, the flat was invaded by a flock of blue butterflies. The sky was tinged a dark blue color never seen before in the neighborhood.

"Your grandmother has found us," Mother whispered softly to my sister that early spring day. "She has come to be present at your wedding. Make certain that from now on you leave a glass of water and a slice of bread on the night table for her to quench her thirst and fill her stomach. She will be staying with you until you are with child. My own grandmother did the same with me."

My sister did not question Mother's assertion. Each day she rose before sunrise to see that the water had been drunk and the bread eaten. She filled the space around the night table with the most beautiful flowers she could find and devotedly replaced those which withered. But my sister did not actually see our grandmother move about the apartment until the night before her wedding. As she retired that night (I can still see the full silver moon bathing on a lone cloud from the kitchen window) I heard Mother tell her that the time had arrived to make preparations for the person who had been watching over her.

"Wash yourself with the special soap I made for you and spray the holy water I brought from the village on the four walls of your room," she advised. Before closing the door to her room, my sister put away her dolls, placing them one by one inside the wooden chest at the foot of her bed.

Father had returned home earlier than usual that night from the barber shop. The customary letter writing to Sheshi took most of the evening. No one ever dared ask him to whom he wrote those letters. Years afterwards I searched in every closet of the apartment and in the deepest recesses of my memories for the name of the person destined to receive those missives. The search was fruitless until the very end of my days, when the name appeared before my eyes as clearly as the first star in the sky, although the sound of that name died within me. Someone, whose name I could not recall at that moment, had told me that Mother sealed the envelope containing the letters with wax and placed it inside the coffin so that Father could finish writing them whenever he could on the other side of the dark wall. It might have been my great-aunt who told me, for she had nurtured Father since the day of his birth and returned to prepare his departure from this life.

I remember that fall afternoon I had been placed on the front porch of the house with a brown woolen cover over my knees. I followed the clouds as they drew moisture from the winding brook. It was going to rain. It must have been close to twelve o'clock when I felt my lids drop tightly over my eyes. With my right ear I barely heard the clock come to a halt. A bright light emanated from a deep tunnel. It turned the air into a heavy silence. An array of timeless faces made their way from the end of the tunnel like so many fading stars. Long-knifed fingers kept the faces away from the countless flower buds from which tongues of fire sprayed flashing stars. A wind came fluttering from the depths of the sky, sowing flocks of bluebirds. I clawed into the memories of the past.

The day before my sister's wedding I had told my mother of a persistent bad dream. "It was not a dream," she had calmly explained as she cleaned the kitchen table. "Your grandmother came to stay with us after journeying through many lands and seas for fear of being forgotten by her family and the people of Sheshi. Times are changing faster now than at any other time."

I realized how heavy a burden forgetfulness can be if

182

there is no sound that laces together the moments of silence. "A dead person," Mother had said that morning, "can only find peace in the mind of those who will nurture their secrets with remembered details." I felt that Mother was completely aware of the details of my dream, and I did not pursue it. "Don't even attempt to relate the dream to me," she then added, "because it is useless. There are no words to relate that event. No one has ever been able to cross with open eyes into the realm of burning light."

So I pursued the matter no further. I decided, instead, to select those sounds, among those with which I was familiar, that could reveal to me the inner working of the dream. With the arrival of our grandmother, my sister had ceased to be a child. She acquired the habit of keeping the house orderly, and she stayed away from her dolls. In fact, having taken over all the chores, she became the center of all things in the apartment. As for Mother, she retired to the softness of her rocking chair where she had begun to crochet a woolen blanket with ninety-nine squares, no two of which were alike. Years later she went on to make woolen slippers as soon as the first cold winds of fall began to blow. But a veiled look of sadness appeared in her eyes that could not be seen during the late afternoon hours. I thought it was the end of the day that saddened her, gnawing ever closer to her bones, but, as I spread the woolen blanket over her knees, I heard her complain that she could no longer battle an intense feeling of boredom. "I am unable to reorder my memories as I try not to lose them. They seem to fade away from me, to the point that I do not even recognize them sometimes."

I assured her that I would gather all the photographs she had brought with us or received from Sheshi. "It is only a matter of identifying the pictures and writing a date on the back of each. That is the way to prevent the bridge from coming apart." In response, she closed her eyes and fell asleep. I was never to see such a peaceful expression upon her face again until the last days of winter, when spring was ready to burst with new sounds and fresh colors. A short time later, the photographs that I had gathered for her from all the drawers of the apartment became the steps that Mother descended and ascended, showing only a furtive smile every now and then as if to demand more information about the pictures. She touched each photograph, feeling every contour. In no time, she was able to order them chronologically in her mind. She left an empty space between the photographs brought from Sheshi and those taken in the flat since our arrival.

Father spent hours with tears in his eyes going through the photographs with Mother every night. He spoke at length about each one, always hoping to notice a smile that would indicate her recognition. They both had changed so much over the years, which weighed upon them ever more heavily with each passing season. Father's dream of saving enough so that we all could return to Sheshi slowly slipped away as he struggled to pay the mounting medical bills.

"It is a gradual deterioration of the liver," one of the doctors attending her ventured to say in a language Father struggled to understand. "The liver will eventually wear itself out," added the doctor's assistant. The cold tones of the two professionals created in my father a feeling of helplessness that was to mark him for the rest of his years. But it was the nurse's demand that she be paid even before she made her examinations that made Father visibly angry. "These people have hearts of stone and the selfishness of hyenas," he sputtered as we made our way back home.

Thus began for Father a growing sense of disillusionment that grew to silent frustration as he watched his family come apart. A few years later he was to shut his eyes completely to whatever surrounded him. As days came and went, he fell deeper and deeper into a profound stupor.

On the other hand, my sister took hold of the house and began to arrange things in her own way. The wedding date was postponed. She announced her decision with unwavering determination. "My mother will get better very soon, and we will have plenty of time to set a new date. It will be only a matter of months."

This, then, became the point of conversation as they spoke with each other, she from the window of her room, he leaning against the lamppost. Little did he know that he would grow old waiting night after night with admirable patience, always clothed in his best suit and shiny yellow tie, just to get a glimpse of her. That was all that he needed to gather the strength for the next evening. He spent the morning washing and ironing the yellow tie. The whole neighborhood knew when it was time to look for him at the only lamppost in the street. The perfume that he wore forced all the neighbors to open their windows so that they might take deep breaths of the rosy air that spoke of love of old.

"If you don't stop languishing, I shall close my window forever," my sister told him one rainy evening. "You have become the laughingstock of the neighborhood!" I could not hear his answer. The wind and the rain had picked up speed, and an agonizing howling had taken over the night. That was the last time I was to see him. He had just begun to pluck the petals from the bouquet of flowers he had brought with him. Later I learned that he had continued to wait beneath the window for years, even though my sister closed the window and secured it with long silver-colored nails. She erased the wedding date from her mind and dedicated her youthful years to saving from forgetfulness the memories of the family.

The clocks in the house were set to six in the evening, for it was the only hour that Mother could recognize. That was the hour when the men of Sheshi returned from the fields and the women set the table for the evening meal. Day after day she relived the same moment on the clock, yet she always approached it from a different angle.

Sister had assumed Mother's personality. The only thing that separated the two was the number of wrinkles on each one's forehead.

By this time I had ventured beyond the front steps of the tenement building. The grocery store operated by the Jewish couple had disappeared. The only thing that remained of it was an old aluminum sign with illegible letters crisscrossing one another like so many geometric figures.

The benches from Saint Mary's park a block from Jackson Avenue had finally lost their battle against the cold winter nights. Tall grass had invaded the once neatly kept lawns, and every cavity was filled with discarded Coca-Cola bottles. The tall cement wall where most of the young men of the neighborhood played together by hitting a small pale red ball against it had crumbled, leaving only the corroded steel beams standing. The signs at every entrance to the park spoke of the sadness of the place. "Closed to pedestrians. Violators will be prosecuted."

The park had been the breathing space of the neighborhood enclosed by the fast-moving car lanes on both sides of the area. The benches that once had known so many retirees, each so different from the other in appearance and gesture, had vanished, taking with them the worlds of old that the elders had secretly protected in the most intimate recesses of their memories.

There had been one old man who had stood out from the rest. In his hands he held a necklace of wooden beads that he touched as he recited some kind of prayer to himself always in the late hours of the afternoon with the sun about to set. Next to him lay a book of prayers and an old newspaper. From time to time he got a pen and a sheet of paper from his pocket and, after lifting his eyes towards the blue of the sky, he wrote a series of signs that looked more like scimitars than letters. His eyes would finally settle on the wall where the young men hit the ball with all their strength.

By the end of October the trees that lined the street that led to the park had just a few leaves still hanging from their branches. The dark clouds that appeared with each passing day were the first harbingers of colder days to come. Still the old men would not stop coming to the bench that faced the cement wall, although only a few young men continued to hit the ball against it. The elders sat in silence while securing a cane beneath their crossed hands and watched them play handball.

A few of the hardy ones kept on coming to the park until the first frost blanketed the benches in white. I always wondered how they spent the long winter months with snow storm after snow storm that kept even the younger ones at bay in their homes. It was at this time that fierce storms came down from Canada and turned every window in the neighborhood into an icy mirror on which the sun's rays sculpted white stars. On that day I was to go to City College for an interview. I was barely able to hide the feeling of elation that I felt in receiving the letter, but I did not break the good news to my family. Mother had been enclosed in her own distant world for quite some time, and my sister had taken complete charge of the family. Father, still bent upon saving all he could to take his family back to the village, lived for the barber shop.

I had tried before applying to City College to work at a textile industry in the garment section. In Sheshi I had been an apprentice to a tailor during the after school hours. The factory owners in their dark long suits were complete strangers to me. They looked unlike any other people I had ever come across before. The putrid air that circulated in the place with hundreds of sewing machines, one moving faster than the next, aroused in me the deepest nausea and at the same time a feeling of sadness at seeing the operators of the machines moving like so many controlled puppets. Sweat rushed down their faces. Their posture betrayed the anxiety of those living in fear after a forced separation from familiar faces.

I thought of Tuliuci and of the many afternoons I had spent in his tailor shop. His words to me, as he fed the black raven in the wooden cage he himself had made from wild bamboo filaments, sounded as true to me now as they might have been to him at the time: "The city with the buildings that pierce the sky that everyone dreams about in Sheshi and hopes one day to reach, is pure hell. There people are placed in large rooms as big as the biggest wheat field along the brook, and they work from dawn until sunset. The air they breathe sticks to their skin like the pitch that falls from the pine trees in early September." The workers, their eyes fastened upon the flying needles, were mostly women. Although their features were distinct, an invisible sense of their solidarity seemed to unite and defend them from the hawkish glances of their supervisors, who strolled back and forth down the center alley of the factory floor.

I was placed at a machine in a far corner of the shop; to my right was a small window, its glass cracked. The rooms I could peek into from where I sat seemed no better than the one we occupied. What I saw was the same cage with the same fake green on the window sills. At the end of the day, as the sky darkened, I told the supervisor that I was not coming back. His response was an immediate burst of anger. "I need you to check for any imperfection in the suits you were working on!" he shouted. His was the sort of anger that I had only encountered in the stray dogs that searched for scraps of food on the outskirts of our village. He followed me to the exit of the factory, screaming at the top of his lungs.

The air outside felt fresher than it ever had before, even though it was laden with humidity. I walked for hours, following street after street with signs that changed little in color until I reached a small park and sat down on the only bench. I watched the birds pecking frantically at bits of food left behind by the children who had been playing there. Pitch darkness fell quickly upon the place, followed by a silent drizzle that escaped even the sense of touch.

I drifted back to my first day in school in Sheshi. A feeling of lightness had taken hold of me, and it demanded no explanation. In the classroom the air smelled of almond flowers. The soft drizzle falling gently bathed each flower on the tree outside the open window. Ten of us sat on the first two rows of chestnut benches; our black uniforms with white collars lent us an air of orderliness. The schoolteacher, who came from the snow-capped mountains of the north, wore a smile that no one in Sheshi had ever seen before. Within just a few weeks, the teacher had gotten to know each of us in such way that there was no secret in us that he did not expose. There was no one among the ten of us who did not wish to please him.

"We have to rebuild what the war has destroyed," he reminded us at the beginning of each lesson. The schoolteacher was unlike any other person in the village. He told the village authorities that he was from the city in the far western part of the country. His hair was bleached by the sun, and his light eyes were like those of the people painted by artists of an age long gone but whose dreams are still with us.

To the women of Sheshi, the schoolteacher was an angel sent by God to lead the children on the path to Heaven. "Do not even try to find the place he is from in the geography book of Prefti Vlasë," the women whispered softly to one another. "He is not of this earth."

The sun from behind the seven mountains was casting a long shadow over the village square. It was in early October. The grapes were ready to be harvested, and the leaves on the olive trees had turned bright silver. The gentleness of the schoolteacher's movements and the whiteness of his hands had become the talk of the women at the wash basin of the fountain in the square. The schoolteacher walked and talked in the square with peasants and landowners alike, a behavior that pleased some and angered others. The peasants sought his advice when it came to selling their grapes and olives to the merchants from the big cities of the north. In just one cycle of time, he had won their trust away from the priest or the doctor of the village. At harvest time, he calculated the amount of their produce and the percentage they owed to their landowners. Even the medicine prescribed by the doctor would not be taken until the contents and the dosage were verified by the schoolteacher. Until then, the people of Sheshi had only resorted to seeing a doctor if the old woman of the village could not identify the ailment that afflicted them. "God wants you to keep Him company. There is nothing that I can do." That was the answer she gave them when she could not isolate their illness with the right mixture of herbs. But now my classmates whispered in the schoolteacher's ear, "My father wants to know if you can come by the house after dark without anyone's seeing you." He never failed to satisfy their wishes or to put their mind at ease. He had learned how to fulfill their needs without threatening the delicate social fabric of the village.

On Sunday afternoons, the schoolteacher climbed the tallest of the seven mountains to drink from the fountain of effervescent waters. In a very short time all the villagers came to consider him as a rare being sent by the grace of God. They felt blessed by his presence and went out of their way to stumble upon him just to have the chance to look into the depths of the sky hidden in his eyes. After Sunday Mass the men openly compared the eyes of the schoolteacher to the Gates of Paradise as they recalled the sermon of Prefti Vlasë. "The Lord gave you sight so that you might glimpse into His soul and know that He is to be found within you and nowhere else."

For all of Sheshi, God dwelled in the deep blue of the eyes of the schoolteacher who had come from so far away to reveal to them that God truly existed. The doors to their homes flung open and their lights shone more brightly when he passed by and filled their rooms with the presence of God. No one ever dared ask him in exactly which city had he been born; no one questioned him about his family. The news of his arrival on the six o'clock train that came from the wheat fields east of the seven mountains spread like a cloud floating on top of the warm winds that had begun to arrive from Africa. "He is not like us; he is just passing by," murmured the elderly to one another as they watched the water flow from the fountain in front of their bench. "His hands are as white as goat's milk," added the women at the basin of the fountain, where the men could not hear a word. Indeed, for Prefti Vlasë it was no surprise that the young girls confessed to him that they dreamed nightly of the young schoolteacher's caressing them with those milky hands.

When a decision was to be made concerning the distribution of water for irrigation or to whom to sell the produce of grapes and olives, the peasants only trusted the schoolteacher. "He was sent here to look after us and to make certain that we are not cheated simply because we were never taught to read. He does not need a sack of stones, like our fathers did, to count," said the one who stood in front of the group.

"I have been told by my grandson that the schoolteacher counts in his mind and not on his fingers," said another.

"It is God's doing," added the one who had spoken first, "for no one can see how he counts."

It wasn't long before the schoolteacher was receiving all sorts of marriage proposals from every young girl in the village. His answer, always carefully crafted to avoid offending anyone, was ever the same: "My heart is not ready to open up yet; it has its own rules that no one can decipher." There was no woman in the village who did not like that reply. In fact, it was a further indication that the schoolteacher really was a rare being. Years would go by before he would choose a woman to care for. By that time, most of the girls had become mothers themselves.

The one who became his wife was a young girl whose age no one could tell and who had come to claim him as her husband from a nameless village. The schoolteacher's future wife arrived in Sheshi along the road that led to the cemetery ...a dirt road which had no beginning but definitely had a clear end. The road was as wide as the iron gate in front of the old part of the cemetery. The young girl's arrival occurred at a time in which many of the young men who had been sent to war to kill an enemy whom they had never seen were returning to the village in rags and terribly diseased. They had aged so much that even their mothers had difficulty recognizing them. "War is like a mask that sticks to your skin and changes you forever," my Grandfather Zelmi used to say. He knew, for he had fought in many far away places and had seen soldiers who simply could not stop killing for fear of falling into boredom.

The schoolteacher met the young girl who had been searching for him at the crossroads below the train station. The village was covered with a thick fog that during the night had made its way up from the deep gorge where the waters of the winding brook descended into the ancient cave of the serpent. For the schoolteacher it was the hour of his customary morning walk through the olive groves to check on the disease that afflicted the centennial trees from within. At the stone next to the spring of the fizzing waters he caught sight of the young girl dressed in white who was destined to become his lifelong companion, outliving every other woman in the village and silencing forever all the other hearts that beat for him. It was the moment he never tired of recounting years later to those who asked him where he had gone to meet the one who had brought back to him that past that had been erased from the well of his memories. "I seemed to recognize her from a moment in time I could not hold down, but I knew at that moment that she was part of me." The young girl stood up as the schoolteacher approached the spring and gave him the smile that his heart had been waiting to feel. They said very little to one another. She simply followed a few steps behind him.

Supported by the cane he himself had carved from an olive tree branch, the schoolteacher took the road through the grove that led to the oldest part of Sheshi. He wanted to get back before the cool breeze of the late afternoon that brought everyone out of their homes. "We reached the first homes of the village in the late evening," he recalled. "The sky had so many stars and the air was so completely still." Even the elders in the main square would remember for years to come the evening when the sky seemed to weave a blanket of silence over the entire village. The only noise that the schoolteacher was able to recall years later was the squeaking of his shoes which had suddenly grown too small for him.

From that night on, the whole village stopped paying attention to the schoolteacher. One late autumn afternoon, after an emotional discussion of the "Brothers Karamazov," the schoolteacher let his feelings flow like a gush of water.

"At first," he said, "I was too involved in putting things in order at the house with the new guest to notice the changes that had been brewing in people's minds. But the first days of winter that followed that turbulent fall made me aware of the aura of loneliness that surrounded us. From the window, I saw a small sparrow freeze to death. My companion, whose name, at first, I could barely make out, spent most of the day tending to the fire. She had not yet ventured out of the house. She swept the floor and did the washing at night. As for myself, I never did have a chance to explain to Prefti Vlasë that we were not living in sin."

On the first Sunday of winter, Prefti Vlasë did announce to the parishioners that he was taking over the teaching in the village. That Sunday also marked the first of the thirty-three sermons that the priest delivered before the tragedy struck that enveloped the oldest section of Sheshi in a mantle of darkness that was to last forever.

Chapter Seven

The worst began around the end of February. Rubina awakened, having spent the night on the wooden bench near the fireplace with a slight fever that reddened her cheeks. She was then the oldest woman living in the village. Her breath still smelled of the pomegranate that only grew on the eastern coast across the narrow corridor of turbulent seas. The icicles on the red roof tiles glittered as brightly as the canopy of stars when she spoke for the last time. She stood at the fountain in the main square, unable to remember the road home. I led her to the first homes of Sheshi carved inside the mountain. In her face I recognized the whole of Sheshi. Rubina died that same night. She washed and anointed herself with oil, put on the only dress she had kept inside an old oak chest, and climbed onto the tall bed. When they found her, the dress she wore was full of swallows about to spread their wide, dark wings. Those who remembered her from years past buried her in the lonely pine grove they still call "the whispering pines." Two weeks later, in the midst of the heat wave, we departed for the city of the playing waves.

I have been standing in front of three college officials who are to admit me into the college program. The wait has been long, and the blue-eyed school teacher in Sheshi has been my companion. There were four of us in the brown-paneled room. An oval table separated me from the officials of the review board. I tried to study their expressions with the hope of anticipating a certain conclusion, but it was like walking through the streets of Sheshi on a night of thick fog in the month of November. Their posture and their inscrutable faces were a copy of the attitude of the immigration officers in the office of the consulate in the city of the singing waves. Two of the college officials did exhibit a vacuous sense of pride, which they made no effort to hide, but the third attempted to display a distant smile that carried within it a vague sign of encouragement. I could see it written in his eyes. The color of those eyes was not unlike that of the school teacher's eyes in Sheshi.

I knew then that I could not let my first teacher down. It seemed as if the time which had passed between the two different worlds had stood as still as the front gates of the village cemetery where the cone-shaped pine trees weaved wreaths of silence in eternity. There the unheard sounds of the tombstones plant new seeds onto the mirrors of the night. "Everything you see," advised the school teacher in Sheshi, "has a hidden side. You must find the way to see it and to sense the energy that moves it."

By that time, his visions, once clear, had become as dark as a stormy sky, but he must have felt a bottomless urge to warn us. Little did he know that he was lifting the veil from our dreams and shattering the world of fantasy much as the swallow that pecked against the sky while chasing the flying ants which the warm spring air often brought to the village.

At the college, I was asked to wait outside. I sat next to two other students who, waiting to be interviewed, were conversing in their own language. Their faces were similar to those on the posters which hung in full view on the front wall of the classroom in Sheshi. One of the figures on the poster sported a thick moustache like the one Grandfather had; he trimmed it before he went down to the main square to take his seat among those who shared his views on politics. The other, who stood behind in the poster, had curly hair and thick glasses which made his eyes look like two sunken wells. Only years later did I learn who they were.

The student stood when his Slavic name was called. Still I

had not been given an answer. I began to feel uneasy, unable to cling to the vanishing smile of the third official. Through the Gothic window I could see that night was falling. In order to return home I would have to walk through an area that most students avoided. Finally, my name was called.

"I can see from your application that you want to pursue a career in the Humanities," said the one with the distant smile.

"Yes, I do," I answered in an assured tone, hoping to relay my unwavering commitment to the field of study. At that time the college was home to dozens of refugees like myself who were full of questions but with very little hope of ever finding complete answers. I realized that afternoon how difficult it was going to be to enter the rigid world of the three people who had interviewed me at City College of New York.

I was asked to wait outside the conference room. I felt a strong urge to run away from the place. An hour later the door to the conference room opened. One of the three interviewers instructed me to choose the fall courses with the help of an advisor. "You will receive a formal letter of acceptance within the week, and in it you will find the name of your advisor," he said without even blinking once. I bowed with respect and left the Gothic building. Night had already fallen, and the wind was buffeting the leaves about on the ground as it despoiled the trees of the few others which yet struggled to cling to the branches.

The few lampposts that lined the street were quickly losing their brightness as a thick fog descended upon the tenements. The entrances to those buildings exhaled a haze of loneliness as the street signs began to float in mid-air. The wet wind kept everyone at home, but for a few homeless people who moved slowly along the iron rail fences with no clear destination in mind. On the main avenue, others walked toward the iron bridge which connected the two boroughs of the city; they were intent upon reconstructing their cardboard homes for the night beneath the steel beams. The staircases to the basements of the tenement houses reeked of urine and of the mold which had clung to them for decades.

I hastened my pace, hoping to make it across the drawbridge before it closed to surface traffic and opened for commercial boats. As I hurried, I thought of Mother, her face pressed to the windowpane, awaiting the return of all her children. She never retired to her own room until she had counted all of us with the green rays of her eyes.

The clock with the golden arrows on the commercial building at the other end of the drawbridge pointed to ten o'clock. That bank building outshone all the others in the vicinity and even pierced through the dense mantle of fog. The marble columns that supported its portico spoke of an age long forgotten by the few who had ever known that it existed. No one, perhaps, could see the long tentacles that crept into the steel safety boxes packed with dreams far and wide of the illuminated building. It was, indeed, the only monument visible from both sides of the East River whose waters flowed to the beat of the drums and the hoarse notes of the saxophones that emanated from the inner recesses of the tenements. On Friday nights, the workers of the city gathered in those places to plant their dreams. They came from miles away to be with the people they recognized and to have conversations that mimicked the rhythm of the musical instruments they knew so well.

The sounds that I heard as I walked along the avenue after class were like the sounds of the long knives the men in Sheshi used to slaughter the pig in celebration of the Christmas season. Each beat opened centuries-old wounds as it told the story of someone who would never have a chance to relate it to any other or to put it down in writing. The sounds were unlike any others with which I was familiar. Within those notes were the sorrowful faces of men and women, and it was not easy to tell who was laughing or who was crying with each beat.

Along the avenue, there were dozens of underground places where any sort of blasé thing took place. From the doors left ajar for a breath of fresh air could be seen long tunnels illuminated by green and red lights floating on grayish-black smoke. The music cried with the tears of long ago, and the indecipherable verses settled upon the faces of those people who occasionally emerged. The anger that hovered about these places was soon suffocated by the strong odor of alcohol and the thick veil of smoke. Within, tall, thin women swirled with the sound of music, though barely anyone paid any attention to them. The stage set in the far corner seemed to float on streaks of red and green lights. Long lines of silent eyes fixed their gaze on the half-filled glasses in front of them. Some patrons begged for a refill without uttering a word. Dollar bills moved on the counter like so many insects. The thin-waisted dancers moved like silhouettes carving through invisible walls of silences packed together by bands of heavy smoke. The contortions of their bodies were those of snakes looking to hide within the overgrowth of the meandering old river still smothering the unheard cries of the night. A wilted rose pinned to the bodice of each dress contrasted poignantly with their bony bodies, chiseled with patience from the branch of a redwood tree, one like those that grow in the deepest gorge of the seven mountains. The singing of the blues that spoke of bad times and broken homes turned everyone's attention to the stage. Eyes melted underneath the black eyelashes.

I thought of Serafina and her singing and dancing outside her home on the road to the train station of Sheshi. She sang of the sunset that took her husband away, never to return from the wide steppes of Eastern Europe. Her voice was so sweet that all the women behind the closed doors of Sheshi thought that underneath every pain there was sweetness. She sang until the burning sun set behind the seven mountains. It was the moment in which the endless line of young men dressed in their best suits and floating in perfumes waited to see Serafina turn into a slender spotted leopard.

This was the talk of the village café, night after night. I would not have believed it, had I not seen it myself. There were three of us, and, for the first time, we had been allowed to sit with the elders in the café. The next day we decided to hide behind the prickly bushes that every other year brought the biggest blackberries in the county. I was the eldest of the three. The other two came from well-to-do families, so our friendship was kept a secret. The caste system that had ruled life in Sheshi for as long as everyone could remember allowed no possibility of questioning it. The wait seemed an eternity, but, as soon as the few clouds which had covered from view the full moon of the early evening vanished, the door to Serafina's stone house opened, throwing into the air lashes of fire and gray smoke. For the first time we saw the familiar legend of the serpent in the sacred cave reach into the magical depths of the night and sensed the awakening of strange, unfamiliar pains that reached deep into the unmentioned depths of secular energy. It was the journey into the heart of that strange desire that had made us tremble when least expected.

The tall, bony figure had stopped dancing and now

directed a piercing glance at a stranger who stood motionless at the entrance of the bar. The Gothic structure of City College was no longer visible. I moved towards the bridge, hoping to cross it before it elevated its steel beams to allow the barges through. As the years were swept away by the cold, autumn winds, so were the faces of the people lined along the avenue from the college to the bridge. Yet, there was one face that refused to succumb to the beatings of time. She was the guardian of the dark, strange world I yearned to enter, a world whose sounds and movements spoke to me of the beatings of a life so pristine and earthly and yet fleeting as the clouds that danced around the moon during those nights.

The old woman carried a plastic bag filled with what appeared to be her own clothes. She seemed to be relying upon a cane, as one shoulder stood lower than the other. Her hair, rumpled and unwashed, guarded a face cross-hatched by hundreds of lines that hid her real self. The distance between the underground bar and the spot where the woman stood was no distance at all. Time moved in a straight line, fusing the starting point with the end point. The waters beneath the bridge were as dark as the sky. I turned around to glance at the woman whom I had left behind. She had covered herself with a white plastic sheet that was no protection from the cold wind channeled by the steel beams of the bridge. For a moment I thought of the three academicians who had conducted the interview and wondered if they had ever crossed the bridge over the dark, silent river.

"Old age is an invisible disease that no one can trace. Go and find the road that begins from beyond the pine trees of the cemetery. Do not think about us. We shall wait for you inside the mirror of our ancestors." This was the elders' way of saying good-bye to the young men of Sheshi as they passed the square through the lined almond trees on their way to the train station. No one of them looked back, and the elders themselves on the wooden bench fixed their eyes on the fountain. The children swirled around their motionless gaze, and the swallows dived forcibly in and out of the breeze that swayed the cross on the belfry.

"No one in the village has ever gone through the wall that rings around the wooden bench of the elders," my mother asserted as I inquired of their whereabouts in Sheshi. "The key to open that door will be given to you when you are ready to enter it and never leave it. Of that road," she continued, "you can only see the beginning. The end, they say, lies beyond the tall cypress trees that in the early days of autumn hide their tops inside the thick fog of the seven mountains."

It must have been about ten o'clock that evening when I saw the two police cars stop near Saint Mary's Park on the main road that crossed Jackson Avenue. The otherwise busy avenue, lined with sycamore trees empty of their leaves, was totally deserted. Most of the lights in the park were out; some were broken, while others lay down, uprooted. Four major paths crossed each other to form smaller ones that disappeared behind the tall bushes. Three officers sprang from the police car swinging batons. In their midst was a small, shirtless man. Tied to the fence, he was repeatedly kicked and struck upon the head. This all happened very quickly. I held my breath until I saw the police car speed away and melt into the silence of the night. I approached the unfortunate man only to see the blood gushing from his head and forming a pool into which his head sank ever more deeply.

I took the path that ended on Jackson Avenue and

quickly entered the apartment building. In the apartment, Mother was still awake with the quilt over her knees. I saw no need to tell my sister what I had witnessed on the avenue. It would only have heightened her fear of the outside. She was listening to some songs that spoke softly of the moon and the seas with a sky filled with stars. I could see her eyes filled with tears which quickly turned into icy streaks as they attempted to fall towards her cheeks. Her heart had hardened the day she told her suitor not to show his face again below her window. "I cannot waste my time with you when I have my mother to care for," she had told him. She did not know that the man leaning against the lamppost was willing to wait for her for an eternity. And, in fact, the people on Jackson Avenue saw him pace from one end of the street to the other even when the neighborhood changed so much that they no longer recognized one another.

I washed the blood from my hands. The image of the poor man's face lying motionless on the steel railing of Saint Mary's Park mirrored itself in my palm. For the first time that night I felt the pain of silence that loomed secretively over the wide avenue that cut Jackson Avenue in two. My mother's eyes moved as if she had seen the head of the man drowning in his own blood disturbed only by the few drops of rain that were falling from the tree branches as they trembled in the wind. She extended her hand as she did when she wished to say something. I placed my hand over hers and felt the emptiness of the park and that of the man soaked in blood and rain. I could barely hear my mother's disconnected sounds as she drew me closer to her and whispered softly, "I was mistaken to tell you not to look back at Sheshi as the train was leaving the station. Turn your eyes back, for there time stands still." I felt a trembling in my hand as I detached it from hers. I promised to follow her advice and placed the quilt over her hands.

It was a sleepless night. The agonizing face of the man on the iron fence of Saint Mary's Park holding onto the last breath of life as his eyes bulged from their sockets grew more violently clear as the night gave way to the first streaks of sunlight. Without giving any explanation, Mother had told sister to place a glass of water with a slice of bread on the kitchen table for thirty nights. "It is the only way that poor man can find his resting place," she said to me weeks later. It was at this time that I became aware how much my sister looked like my mother. They had become of one mind. Morning after morning, I found the glass empty and the slice of bread eaten in three places. The five copper pots which hung over the stove changed places nightly, and the light brightened and dimmed with regularity during those thirty days. Yet everything assumed a strange calm just before dawn, when all in the house returned to its original place.

On the morning of the twenty-ninth day, my younger brother was found sleeping on top of the tall bureau between the living room and the bedroom. "Bring him down, but take care not to awaken him," my mother told Sister. "It is the little spirits who roam around during the night and play tricks on the living while the souls of the dead search for eternal rest."

That morning, my younger brother opened his eyes with a fear that even Mother had never seen there before. "He has been marked forever by someone transiting to the other side of darkness," Mother declared as she tried to hold back her tears.

"They are waiting to beat me up!" he told Father, who was concerned that an absence from school would bring the authorities to the house. So it was that I was given the task of accompanying him to school. The fake stone building stood on the east side of Saint Mary's Park. "I have been dreaming of a dead man drowning in his own blood and unable to scream night after night," my brother confided one morning as we approached the school. The horror with which he awoke that morning stayed with him for the rest of his life. Doctor after doctor simply diagnosed it as a chronic pneumonia in one of the lungs which forced the brain to emit distorted images.

"I will be taking you home after school," I told him. "The dream of the dead person is just a fleeting image you must have seen on television." But this did nothing to reassure him. For years he enclosed himself in his room, drawing the face of the dead man tied to the railing that enclosed Saint Mary's Park. Yet, his schoolwork was superb. The rest of his time he devoted to completing the drawing.

"I am almost there. I only need a few more details to capture the fear hidden deeply in the man's eyes," he announced during the evening meal. By this time, Father had difficulties grasping what was being said. His eyes wandered from place to place as if trying to recognize objects.

In no time, all four walls of my younger brother's room were covered with the drawings of the dead man of his dreams. "If he ever opens the closet on the side of the bed, we will never see him again," Mother announced one night as she began to mend the woolen quilt she had brought from Sheshi. It was being slowly consumed by the moths hidden in the four corners of her wooden chest. I was never able to actually see even one of these moths as I placed the quilt over her knees night after night. I saw the colors fade with the approaching darkness of the night only to reappear still faded the next morning. Mother consumed skeins of yarn trying to bring the quilt back to its original condition, but what she mended in a week was consumed in just a few days. The devouring began as soon as she closed her eyes. It wasn't long before her eyes barely opened with the first sunlight of the morning.

Our home became a nest of dreams. Thick walls of silence were being erected around each family member. The usual conversations during the evening meals at the dinner table began to fade away. It wasn't long before each took refuge in a world where sensations and undefined desires moved faster than the dark clouds of a stormy night. The distorted face of the man tied to the iron fence had entered the apartment to stay. The house key was turned to the left from the inside door just before sunset. Many a time the door stayed closed for weeks. That night, I had thought of moving the dead man's head to the east away from the dark clouds enveloping the moon. The thick blood gushing from his mouth and ears had completely masked his face.

I went back to the park night after night to see if his soul had stopped wandering through the loneliness of the deserted paths of the park. The body had vanished and no trace was left of the killing. For a while I even convinced myself that it must have been all a dream, something perhaps seen or read in a moment of distraction caused by the ticking of the clock or the changing hues of sunlight. The blackbirds beating their wings against the fence of the park and the violent shaking of the tree branches that lined the avenue were proof that the beating and the killing had really taken place. These impressions were not caused by the wind, for nothing else moved.

I sought corroboration for what I had witnessed from the newspapers and the evening news and even from a few of the people from the neighborhood, but nothing was mentioned and no one knew anything. "These things only happen in the spy films they show every now and then on television," said the one who sat on the steps to the apartment building.

The darker one who was leaning against the entrance added sarcastically, "Nothing happens in this neighborhood." His stern expression revealed ingrained pains from the past. I dismissed the temptation to refer the event to the men in black uniform in the brick building on the north side of Saint Mary's Park.

The morning coffee was served in silence in the presence of Mother and Sister. Father had left for the barber shop much earlier than usual, hoping, perhaps, to serve the customers he had not served during the week. It was a cloudy Saturday. Little did he know that those clients had moved away from the neighborhood. It was an event that occurred with precise regularity. One group of people would replace another and quickly change the character of the place. Without any order being issued, the houses would be repainted, the flower beds redesigned, and the windows covered with dark brown curtains.

"Out there things happen in ways our family cannot comprehend. In my dreams I have been seeing men in black uniforms digging deeply in underground caves. Black spiders fill the walls and their bellies grow with the taste of blood." Mother had not spoken for months. The lucidity and directness for which she had been known in Sheshi had come back to her. I could see a distant smile work at the corners of my sister's mouth. Perhaps she felt less burdened by the responsibilities of caring for everyone in the family, for Mother's words were proof that she was still in charge in the house. "I will not let you fall into the mouth of the spider," she said to me. "I know too well what I had to endure to bring you into this world. Your sister and your younger brother will soon be depending on you and your father will have to close the barber shop sooner than he thinks. The day he opens his eyes to what is happening around him, he will be forced to let go of the world he has known ever since his first day as an apprentice in the village's barber shop."

What Mother had foretold happened sooner than expected. One November evening as we were seated at the dinner table, Father announced that he would no longer go to the barber shop. "Yesterday," he said, "I waited all day long for a customer; no one came." That night, nothing more was said. The inevitable had been announced to the surprise of no one. What was not expected was the conviction with which Father had delivered his decision.

The winter that followed was longer than usual. Mother and Father spent day after day sitting close to one another by the kitchen window, which overlooked the neatly kept vegetable gardens. The gardens brought smiles and wisps of sadness into their faces as the produce changed colors with the passing seasons. Soon after, my parents began to weave their memories with the light of the changing seasons and the hues of the clouds. No one else in the house disturbed their stay by the window except to serve them their afternoon cup of coffee or to call them to the dinner table.

My younger brother, Darius, whose fear of the dead man on the iron fence of Saint Mary's Park had by now taken over his whole being, double locked the door to his room and took refuge in the closet with his ancient leather globe. "The world is much smaller than it appears to be," he proudly announced one evening as we sat around the table. Darius had suddenly grown into a learned young man with knowledge that went beyond the written words on the leather globe. Indeed, time had taken hold of each member of the family and had begun to build high walls like the ones that grow on top of the clouds on the first days of winter.

On Jackson Avenue, the opposition to the war being fought on the other side of the world grew louder with each passing day. Tall grass was slowly creeping into every path in Saint Mary's Park. The young of the neighborhood no longer played handball against the cement wall. Their older brothers had come back in gray uniforms with brass buttons. Behind their forced smiles lay fears dipped in blood. Death had come to nest on Jackson Avenue.

In the sky, flocks of black birds swirled violently over the chimneys of the tenement buildings. It was then that Mother took hold of my hand with all the strength she could muster and let go a stream of disconnected sounds. "This war will open a wound that will never close, and the first to be sent to the fields of the dead flowers will be those who look like us. Many will never scale the heights of the mountains. The neighborhood will never be the same. Your brother will be with them. When he returns, he will not recognize the house."

The heavy rains that brought fall to an end had arrived much earlier. For weeks the streets adjoining Jackson Avenue remained impassable. Sheets of rain had turned the avenue itself into a river, and heavy debris from collapsed homes and uprooted trees blocked the entrances to the tenement buildings. The elderly could no longer take the usual afternoon stroll that generally affirmed that they were still part of the community and that time had not played any tricks on them. It rained for three full weeks, and it took the sun another week to dispel the dark clouds that had loomed over the neighborhood. On the second morning of the fifth week, the postman delivered a letter with three stamps filled with stars on a clear blue backdrop. I placed the letter on the kitchen table and noticed that it did not carry the name of the sender.

The library stood on the other side of the train tracks that divided the main avenue. In the basement, among the stacks of newspapers, I searched for any news I could find about the death of the man tied to the iron railing of Saint Mary's Park. I received special permission from the librarian to go through the newspapers. Through his thick spectacles, he followed every move I made. We were the only two people to break the mantle of silence that hovered over the large reading room filled with rectangular oak tables. Many a time I was tempted to tell him what I had witnessed that October day at exactly ten o'clock at night. (I knew for certain that it was ten o'clock because I had counted each toll of the bell.) But I restrained myself because of the long streaks of fear I had noticed in the librarian's eyes. These were dark filaments in the shape of whips beating upon naked bodies running toward an open space which became ever more restricted by the buffeting winds as they approached it. The lacerated bodies were beaten repeatedly until they moved no more.

It was a Friday evening. The librarian and I were the only ones left in the reading room. The old woman who usually sat motionless in the corner of the room guarding her two plastic bags filled with newspapers had left earlier. Now the librarian appeared dazed, his mind wandering into the depths of his memories. I could see in his face the vivid picture of a person screaming for air as he faded into the crevices of darkness. I could sense his keen sorrow at having failed to find someone who could hear him and share the pain of his remembered existence. Dragging his left foot, the librarian approached the table. "I must close for the day. You may come back tomorrow to continue with your research."

"I saw someone beaten to death awhile ago near Saint Mary's Park. No one seems to know anything about it. I was hoping to find some news by going through the newspapers," I said.

"Don't waste your time," he admonished. "Such news is not printed." The rain that had been falling for the past hour came crashing against the window panes of the reading room. Darkness had descended, blurring the entire chamber. The librarian locked the doors and shut off the lights.

Outside, the steady rains had already flooded the street. The treetops brushed the sky without reaching the clouds. From a distance I saw the librarian lock the main entrance to the library and then turn to glance at the building with its white columns and rectangular colonial-style windows. The intensity of the rain forced him to hesitate from crossing the street. Soon the quickly rising water compelled him to return to the entrance of the library. With his hands pushed deeply into the pockets of his raincoat, he watched the current depositing all manner of debris along the sidewalk. The sheets of rain that followed the intermittent thunder suffocated the inner cries of the tiny figure huddled against the door. He looked like an untold story kept secret by the shadows of those people who never find a way to lean against something solid and whose lives come and go like the fading colors of the leaves during the last days of autumn.

By now the swift current had reached the first of the library stairs. It seemed to want to rain forever. I moved to the higher ground of the main avenue and waited for the bus to take me home. The librarian had gone inside to wait for the rain to end. Far away along the horizon there appeared an opening of light and dark blues amidst mountains of black clouds. The fallen leaves sailed like thousands of ships aided by the reflected lights of the lampposts.

A week had passed, but the librarian had not been seen

at his desk. I did not dare to suppose the reason for his absence. During the second week, his place was taken by a young woman in her thirties. Her dark hair and thick dark glasses obscured every other feature. She spent every minute of the day dusting and reordering the library cards. The few people who used the reading room were of no concern to her. Soon after she began dusting and wiping the colonies of mold that had invaded the bookshelves. The dark clouds had already begun to fuse with each other into thicker and darker clouds.

It was the first day of December. To be exact, it was also the first Monday of the week. The newspaper I was reading verified the date. I heard the door to the library open. The old librarian appeared. He wore a heavy black coat and a hat that covered his ears. He walked straight towards the table where I sat with the newspaper open. He pulled up a chair quietly, sat down and looked at me with intense anxiety. "I was unable to come to work because a persistent fever took possession of me. It lasted for weeks, which soon seemed longer than all the years I could count. Last night they came to tell me that my position in the library was terminated. I barely had the strength to even open the door to my room. 'Don't ask any questions,' they said. 'The decision is final. It came from high above and there are no procedures for appeal.' They left without even closing the door. I spent the night trying to search my memory for where I had seen them before, but I could trace neither of the two. Maybe you can help me identify them if they ever step into the library."

So began our long mutual wait for the two men to return. Our eyes were fixed upon the entrance to the library. To avoid being detected by the new librarian we learned how to communicate with the movements of our fingers and eyes. I searched through every available magazine, scrutinizing each photograph in them with the hope of tying those two men to the ones who had beaten the hapless victim in Saint Mary's Park. Meanwhile, the elderly librarian dissected the news printed in the community papers to find a reference to his discharge from his post. It did not take long for the pile of magazines and newspapers to attract such suspicious glances from the female librarian that we were cowed into keeping our fingers still and our eyes down.

At home, Mother had taken a turn for the worse. The clarity of her eyes, which had been able to pierce through the fear that besieged me, was no longer. In its place was dark gray cloudiness.

Now the entrances to Saint Mary's Park were patrolled by dozens of police wearing dark blue uniforms and bearing automatic rifles. Shrouded by the dense silence that had invaded our apartment from the alley of the tenement house, I examined inch by inch the spot where the killing had taken place that October night. Had there been someone else that night who might have heard the suffocating voice of the dying man from one of the windows of the building that faced the railing? I asked myself that question over and over again as the sunlight faded in the sky and I gave way to even greater fears rather than gathering the courage to enter that building.

"People only see what they want to see," cautioned the old librarian when I told him of my desire to search for a witness to the killing. But late that afternoon the nauseating image of the man drowning in his own blood compelled me to approach the building facing the railing. It was the tallest structure in the area, its brick face darkened by the exhaust from the automobiles that rushed by. Iron ladders sprung halfway from each window. An old wooden door, weather beaten by the rainy days of fall and the piles of snow of winter, stood ajar. Inside, an old wallpaper designed with barely discernible hunting scenes covered the hallway. The floors were littered with discarded paper and soda cans. Not one of the names on the list of tenement dwellers was legible, so I was not surprised that no one answered when I rang the first three bells of the top section. I went through the entire panel with the same result. The cold, distant atmosphere had choked forever the last of the memories that might have inhabited the premises.

Outside the wind blustered mercilessly, causing the few remaining leaves to cower against the sidewalks. The higher branches of the trees, totally barren, were already shrouded by the cold evening mist that descended from the gray clouds which had hovered above the city for weeks. At a lone window of the dark building two elderly faces hid between the drapes and the shutters. They moved like the colors half-visible between the cracks in the menacing clouds.

I returned home facing the heavy evening traffic on the avenue. Vaguely audible steps followed me to the corner of Jackson Avenue. I walked close to the row of houses with their rusted front railings, a piercing feeling of defeat threatening to invade my whole self. At home alone with Mother, Sister assailed me with a complaint as I locked the door behind me and set the security chain. "We rarely see you anymore."

"I am doing some research in the library," I replied. Mother sat quietly with her eyes closed next to the kitchen window. I approached and touched her left hand softly. She always kept it on top of the woolen blanket, ready to communicate with Sister. The fingers, now all bent and swollen at the joints, trembled incessantly.

Yet Mother's eyes still revealed the deep understanding she had of the surroundings. Her intense look penetrated much beyond the surface of objects, reaching the depths where sound and color fused with deep feeling caused them to oscillate furiously. This often happened at the dinner table, where dishes abruptly changed places. "Things have a life of their own," explained my mother. "They are moved by a force invisible to us but clear as the sky after a summer storm to those who came before us."

Her fingers trembling ever more violently, she added, "Your search will not lead you anywhere." I had a feeling that she had been reading me like an open book ever since I began to follow the movement of her own eyes. She fell into a deep stupor and pointed her two middle fingers toward my sister. "She is saying that one of these days you won't be able to find your way home because you will confuse bats for swallows in the infested alleys of the neighborhood. I will make you an amulet with the bone powder of our dead from Sheshi," she added.

Sister and Mother spoke to one another without uttering a sound. As they moved in and out of their inner space, I could only see the plants blooming with intense yellow flowers that turned into butterflies that searched for the sun's rays meandering through the kitchen ceiling. The china globe of the old electric light had to be emptied every week. Sister carefully placed each butterfly upon a long circular string until she had counted ninety-nine of them, whereupon she positioned them inside blue envelopes. "The blue will help them live longer," she said.

Years later, as I removed the last pieces of furniture from the apartment to move to a single room, I heard the workers who were removing the living room wallpaper exclaim. They had come across thousands of envelopes filled with well-preserved yellow butterflies whose wings displayed a strange linguistic code. Resembling ancient texts, the blue windows with endless words appearing and disappearing in them defied the efforts of the most sophisticated museum officials who sought to decode them with high-powered microscopic lenses. These linguists never realized that the butterfly wings were ingrained with the many conversations between Mother and Sister.

Night had fallen and a heavy, stultifying air had settled over Jackson Avenue. Mother had not stopped moving her two fingers. At times, she even attempted to move her head toward the door to the apartment corridor. Until now, though her joints had become crooked with pain, her face had preserved its youthful expression, her eyes, their typical intensity. She kept a photograph of her mother as a child inside a leather amulet. They had looked like twins in a timeless circle, but over time, Mother's features had begun to retreat.

On a bitterly cold night, the amulet fell to the floor and lay there as dust clinging to the linoleum, as sap upon the bark of a tree. Red drops emerged from the dusty brown mound, and, with a piercing howl, opened a crevice in the floor. The sound was the same as that which descended from the seven mountains on top of Sheshi and forced the inhabitants to nail the windows shut with iron claws. Sister, standing next to the window that overlooked the street, had just imagined seeing Father's bent figure returning from the barber shop when she heard the lacerating cry. "Go and look for Father!" she urged. "Something must have happened to him."

I rushed down the wooden stairway. The streetlights had just come on and the wind howled and banged the door to the building back against the wall. Jackson Avenue seemed to mirror itself in the pale white color of the sky. The street was completely empty. The lights on the front entrances of the private houses trembled with the sheets of cold slashing against them. The main avenue was also deserted of automobiles and pedestrians, and the elevated train on Third Avenue floated silently over the darker lines of the horizon.

I quickened my pace, convinced by now that something indeed had occurred at the barber shop. I feared that Father had been beaten and robbed of the few dollars he managed to earn. I felt as helpless as those faces hiding behind the curtains of the building opposite the pool of blood along the iron railing of Saint Mary's Park.

"We have to go back home before your mother leaves us. She made me promise to bury her between her mother and father." Those were the words Father had said the previous night as he announced that the time had come to close the shop for good. Most of the stores selling affordable clothing had also been shutting their doors for months, leaving the sidewalks along Third Avenue littered with refuse and empty cartons.

Father was sitting in the last chair against the wall. The revolving leather chairs in front of the rectangular mirror had all been slashed. Slumped there motionless, he was slow to recognize me. "We should go home now," he said in a tremulous voice. I lifted him from the chair and helped him to put on his coat. He wiped away the foam that had been spread over the mirror, turned off the lights and locked the door without looking back. The way home was filled with pained silence. Father walked close to me, as if he wanted to hang onto something stronger than he.

This was the third time that they had entered the barber shop and threatened to move the knife placed against his throat. "They were young, not yet men. I could see it in their eyes," he kept repeating as we quickened the pace toward home with the wind howling from branch to branch along the main avenue. The neighborhood, where the barber shop had been for generations, had changed without my father's awareness until those days when he waited for hours for a client to come in. He had been very patient, never losing the hope of building a big clientele and making his barber shop the realm he had dreamt of owning ever since that first morning when his own father had awakened him.

"'Wash you face and comb your hair to the side. I am taking you to Master Basili to learn his trade,'" your grandfather said to me. "I walked close to him, like you are doing now, going down the dirt road that led to the main square of Sheshi, careful not to soil my polished shoes and the white shirt your grandmother had ironed the night before. I can still feel the heavy starch in the collar and cuffs. She had spent the night scrubbing the buttons with vinegar. I had just turned eight years of age three days before. I remember the date very well, for, deep down where I used to hide so many things I could not say, I was wishing that my mother had baked just a few of those sweet Christmas cookies with the white sugar on top. But the day went by just like any other. Mother sat next to the balcony mending the same work clothes that came in rectangular boxes from a faraway aunt. And my father sold shoes to the people who lived on the high slopes of the seven mountains. Owning a pair of shoes in those days was like having a house or a beast of burden now. He always warned people to protect the shoes from the rain and the mud. The pair of shoes you wore when you left Sheshi with your mother and younger brother was the very last pair your grandfather ever made."

As I walked beside Father, I noticed how diminutive he had become. Gone was the pose of certainty and pride that he had struck in the photograph he kept carefully sealed in an old cigar box inscribed in dull yellow letters with the name "La Habana." When I had asked my father what the name meant and where the box had come from, he told me that it had been brought to Sheshi by a sailor who died of homesickness before he could find his way back to the sea. The sailor was a distant uncle of his who had gone around the world in search of a place to make his home. He had stayed away from Sheshi for many years, but when he returned without having found such a place, he realized that the parcel of land he had been looking for stood at the end of the village. From there he could look around one hundred and eighty degrees and see as far as his blurred vision would allow without stepping out of the circle of round stones. The uncle had given my father the cigar box as he, in full sailor's uniform, was being taken to a home in the city beyond the seven mountains where no home had fewer than a hundred steps. It was said in Sheshi that the steps in that city multiplied as one ascended them and finally came to rest in the blue stone church that, on a clear day, disappeared into the depths of the sky.

By now it was drizzling with determination. We had a while to go before reaching home. I was told not to mention anything of the event; little did my father know that Mother had seen everything before it happened. In her moment of lucidity she was able to recall the minutest details of circumstances that would lead to changes in what we were accustomed to seeing. "Things have a soul of their own. They float into spaces to which we have no access," she reminded herself as she tried to control the movement of her two middle fingers. It was only lately that I had begun to realize that Mother's inward eye allowed things to be seen from within, while the rest of us only saw the fleeting moments of those objects as they awakened a memory in ourselves.

"Your mother," continued my father in a sullen voice as we walked as close to the tenement buildings as we could, "is no longer with us. At times I feel that she doesn't recognize me; she must be very unhappy to be here. I should never have allowed her to leave Sheshi. I guess she misses our home and the afternoon visits to the cemetery to converse with her parents. Had I known that she would end this way, I would have fed you wild chicory of the sort that grows down in the village ravine instead of leaving you alone for so many years."

Trying to lessen the guilt that was weighing so heavily upon his conscience I told my father that it was not his fault, that he should blame, instead, the long war that had ravaged the countryside and had brought those strange people to Sheshi who killed all the swallows in the square with their copper bullets and crooked knives just for the fun of it. I had no way of knowing if he understood me, for I received no reply. The wind had turned icy and Father was having difficulty breathing. We slowed our pace and rested at the entrance of a brick building from which I could detect the light in our apartment window. There was a streak of black to one side of the glass; it must have been the shadow of my sister who was waiting for our arrival. Of course we did not know then that it would be her fate to wait a lifetime for some one of us to come home.

"Get used to waiting," Mother advised her. "It is going to be your lot, and no one can change it." Sister was to wait all her life, even putting off her own death, for the invisible suitor who was to take her to the other side of Saint Mary's Park that she could scarcely make out from her bedroom window.

"We can go now," said Father. "I think I can breathe better. Besides, I can see your sister waiting for us from her window, even though my eyes are beginning to betray me." The air had thickened, weighing upon my shoulders as if to prevent me from seeing my father safely home. A sense of sadness nestled deep within me as the drizzle changed into cold drops of steady rain.

Over dinner, the announcement was made. "I shall no longer work at the barber shop." Father did not go into the specifics he had discussed with me. My mother's fingers stopped twitching and, for just a moment, they extended naturally over the woolen blanket covering her knees. Her face seemed to have found the serenity she had been longing for as she sought to meet my sister's eyes. The evening came to an end as naturally as the old season, with the new one already displaying its own changes.

In no time I became the focus of attention and of reliability at home. Father had taken his place next to Mother by the window overlooking the carefully kept vegetable garden. On the sill they had placed a few pots seeded with basil and oregano. Around the plants they wove years of memories together, avoiding, perhaps, the completion of the circle that was creeping up the window through the vines from down below.

The objects that filled the apartment seemed to have found their natural place, and so had my sister, who began weaving the most intricate designs in the white linen she had brought from Sheshi. It was a gift from our great-grandmother. In the late hours of the afternoon, when the sun had begun its descent behind the tallest hill of Saint Mary's Park, Sister glanced into the street from her bedroom window. "I dreamt last night that he had come back," she related to Mother each morning as she prepared the usual cup of black coffee. "I asked some of the neighbors if they had seen him, as they had before, leaning with one leg against the lamppost, his eyes fixed on the front window of the house. Not one of them could recall such a sight."

"Things change too fast for us," one of the neighbors ventured to say. "We can't keep up with them, for we have no space left in our memories."

The sign over the door of the old Jewish couple's store was washed out and people no longer sat on the steps of the tenement homes as they once had upon returning from work. Tall, almost windowless buildings had taken the place of the four-story homes with their iron ladders zigzagging from one window to another. The black lampposts had been replaced with taller aluminum lights that bent down from the sky like lone wires. The automobiles with thick dark windows swept down the avenue like the tail end of comets. People moved in a controlled fashion, as if directed by an invisible hand from behind walls of fog nourished by the approaching winter.

Mother and Father rarely moved from their place overlooking the garden, and my sister learned to ignore the passage of time as she embroidered sheet after sheet without duplicating a single one of her intricate, geometric designs. "I hope I will have enough sheets before I hear the bell ringing from downstairs." She never lost the hope of opening the door for him. But in the neighborhood, she was the only one who still kept seeing him leaning against the lamppost as his face slowly withered.

One morning, toward the hour when the sun shone most brightly, revealing briefly the myriad cracks that had appeared on the walls and the hundreds of spider webs in the many corners, my sister discovered mountains of moths which had been multiplying inside the sheets of fine linen. "Now I know for certain that I will have to wait much longer for the bell to ring. Mending this damage is going to take me many seasons." In a way she thought that it was Mother who had sent the moths into the cedar wardrobe so as to keep her busy with her chores.

At this time the letters we had received regularly from Sheshi had ceased to arrive. In his brief moments of lucidity, Father would ask Sister to go down to the mailbox to check for the mail. "The mailman hasn't come by yet," she would tell him, hoping to extend his interval of clarity so that she could ask him what to do with the barber shop that had been closed for months. "Wait until your older brother decides to join us from the city beyond the white mountains," he asserted with his timeless mind, trying to convince himself that all his efforts had not been in vain. "He will have everything ready upon arrival and will be able to sustain himself and his family." It was this answer that made us aware that Father had returned to the time of his youth and was talking in the same way that his own father had spoken to him when he had decided to close his cobbler shop in Sheshi.

Grandfather had written his son a long, detailed letter from the land of the twin eagles, where he had been sent with his shiny black uniform. In the missive, he had advised my father how urgent it was to return to the village and assume ownership of the shop. "The holidays are approaching," he wrote, "and the young men of Sheshi are getting ready to look their best." My father had kept that letter among his most valuable documents for more than fifty years.

I returned to the library with the hope of seeing the old man with the numbers on his right arm. I waited for days while I resumed reading the newspapers from front to back. One front page bore the picture of soldiers wearing khaki uniforms and long beards. Others spoke of lost struggles against an invisible enemy that fought at night, causing droughts and famine wherever it appeared. From the heartland where the wheat fields grew as tall as poplar trees, people were taking up arms against foreign invaders looking for a better life. Two images on the front page of another newspaper caught my attention because they presented such a stark contrast. On the left of the first page a black woman sat cross-legged; she was holding a child whose ribs protruded from his body like so many dead twigs. An empty wooden bowl stood like an empty water hole between the woman and the child. To the right was the image of a pale, slim woman draped in garlands of gold and silver; she stood next to a brand-new washing machine. The caption read, "Now a woman can protect her soft skin from the damaging effect of detergents."

"Have you seen the old man who sat across from me at this table" I asked the new librarian with the long, curly black hair as she collected the rest of the newspapers.

"I do not pay attention to who comes and goes from the library. Hundreds of people use these facilities every day. Besides, I have been busy dusting and rearranging the books on the shelves," she retorted firmly. In truth, the old librarian and I had been the only ones present in the library for months.

I left the library quietly and walked down Chamber Street for just a few blocks to inquire about the old man at the spot where he stopped daily for a quick cup of coffee. "He was here last Friday just when we were about to close. He left this envelope for you. He knew you were going to come here to ask for him," said the girl as she continued to clean and reset the tables. I opened the envelope as I stepped out of the coffee shop.

"No one was killed on the night of November fourteenth at the front railing of Saint Mary's Park. There was no news of the event in any of the newspapers printed three days before or three days after that date."

Still I waited for the old librarian to come back and to take his seat across from me at the reading table in the library. Autumn passed and the first uncertain snowflakes playing in the wind arrived. I entered the new grocery store, where the elderly Jewish couple had worked, and greeted the owners in their own language. They had come from an island in the Caribbean where the palm trees swayed with the breeze day after day. Bright colors and exotic fruits replaced the indefinable sense of loss that I had always felt as I faced the old Jewish couple.

I left through the back door and paused in every entrance along the street to make certain that no one was following me. I remembered how the old librarian had told me, almost in spite of himself, that he had been hiding from certain pursuers since the morning he found the tall gates of the concentration camp wide open and sheets of silences all around the compound. "The halls of pain were deep in the heart of Poland where the trees grow as thickly as sugar cane," he had said, pointing out the place on the globe in the corner of the reading room. "You don't know what it is to live in fear," he had continued. "Sometimes you wished they would just catch up with you and get it over with."

The idea that the librarian must have given up passed through my mind together with the thought that my own father had now relinquished the very trade that had given him the strength to travel to a new land across that vast ocean only to eventually take his place mutely next to the window overlooking the backyard of the tenement house. His words came back to me: "I am trying to keep your mother's hand from slipping away. One's life is a long wait; at times it is undertaken alone, other times with someone else in mind. But the repose that is sought from the time we open our eyes until we close them again is to be found in the changing colors of the seasons and in the flower seeds falling to the earth."

Where could the old librarian have gone? There were very few places to hide in the city. Most of the entrances to the tenement buildings had been padlocked and the air was redolent with the odor of the burned fat that seeped from the drains. Just a few blocks and I would be able to see the window of his apartment. The streetlights had not yet been lit, and I did not feel the presence of anyone. From time to time an automobile sped by as if it too pursued another.

Something told me to turn back. I entered the "Happy Bar" on Adam Street. The men seated in a row at the counter fixed their eyes either on the mirror or on their glasses filled with beer or whiskey. From the corner where I sat I could hear their heavy breathing. They looked like endless rows of men condemned to the gallows, their faces revealing old wounds.

Smoke settled defiantly over the dim red lights of the counter. The street had been taken over by the darkness of night. The few remaining people had fallen quiet. The jukebox stood soundlessly in the corner facing the pool table. There a lonely player moved back and forth adjusting and readjusting the one ball as he answered his own questions aloud in a way that would have deceived anyone unable to see him. The bartender looked at me, sensing that I was there by chance. "If you are here to hide, it is best that you know that they won't come in here. They might be waiting for you outside."

A knot formed in my throat, so that I was unable to say anything for a moment. When I looked at him and nodded, the gesture assured him of my appreciation. The man at the pool table put change into the jukebox and pressed the buttons for his songs. The hands of the clock on the wall behind the counter appeared not to move. The slow beat of the music began to take over the place, and the only person seated at the counter was tapping his fingers to the familiar rhythm, his mind floating to places accessible only to him. Invisible walls separated each of us from one another.

The shivering sound of the East River nearby gnawed at an abandoned riverboat, the dark waters choking the last lament with iron chains, while the slow tapping on the bar counter was busy closing the wounds of old. The red had turned to brown on the trunks of many of the trees lining each side of the river. The sun dove behind the horizon just as it had done for centuries, unmoved by the cries of the wind that knit together hunger and humiliation. Dreams clung to the sky like sharp needles to the hardened skin of the man gulping his last drink. The empty glasses, like so many scattered sacred stones, refused to foretell the future. The words from the jukebox sang of golden paths deep into the blue of a clear sky. The city fell sound asleep in white linen sheets like a voiceless and unfeeling womb creating life in silence. The night had imprisoned the sounds inside the white parchment of artistic drawings held sacred by the select few. The tapping had ceased completely by the time the man at the pool table turned to throw his last dart against the dartboard. He was a dark, unshaven figure, his hair laced back by a green thread, his swollen eyes ringed with dark patches. There was deep anger hidden in this man.

"He has been coming here since last year," said the bartender as he placed the glass of wine I had asked for on my table. "No one knows where he came from. Would you like anything else?"

The door had not opened since I had come in. I thought of the old librarian's warning. "They will never give up following you; even in your dreams, you won't be able to get rid of them."

The bartender had not taken his eyes from the man shooting darts, although he had not said a word to him all night long. I had always wondered what shape things took when seen from behind the stage. Now, through the thick wall of smoke swirling from corner to corner, I noted that the man who had been tapping had lowered his head onto his crossed forearms. Night had cushioned the flow of water on the East River. The corroded chains barely held on to the riverboat. The tears of women and hungry children quietly washed away, buoys of oblivion suffocated by gray moss from the deep. A bone-deep loneliness reigned over the bar. The man at the pool table had been looking nervously at the clock, which indicated one hour before closing time. "He has no place to go," observed the bartender as he picked up the empty wine glass from my table. "When he leaves here," he continued, "he goes from door to door trying to find one left ajar by someone in a hurry. At sunrise he moves to the park just a few blocks from here, passing time by feeding the pigeons with bits of discarded bread."

I felt an inchoate fear taking hold of me. I thought of the stone steps of the Church of the Dead in the main square of Sheshi, where the coolness of the evening hours would be making its way to the water fountain. The moonlight would soon fill the air with bright, crystalline dew gently falling on the blades of grass, determined patches of life growing among the rocks. The line of steps grew dimmer as the hours rolled by only to be replaced by the image of the raised skin of my mother's hands.

I had left the basement bar the way I had found it. The

bartender had begun to wash and dry the few glasses over and over again. The man with the crooked, tapping fingers had buried his head deeper into his arms, and the drifter at the pool table had begun to chalk the billiard stick. Night hovered firmly over the neighborhood. The cool air fogged the few streetlights still standing. A furtive wind had brought an intermittent drizzle, and there was silence everywhere. The waters on the East River, stilled by the cold air, seemed like an old mirror with streaks of black running through it. Beneath its surface the remaining drops of life moved inexorably toward the deep silences of the ocean. The steel bridge covered with the loneliness of times past wavered between the starless sky and the murky waters below. Two tugboats, bows lowered, plied the waters, which offered no resistance. It was well past midnight. The clock on the corner bank, with its marble pillars casting every other building around it into shadow, was itself without light.

I could smell death all around Jackson Avenue, just like Uncle Kanjiki could from the moment he returned to Sheshi from the Long War. He came back with his fingers frozen to the bone. His return had prompted all the villagers to think that death was sleeping among them and that terrifying times lay ahead. In no time the townsfolk could smell death everywhere, even on their own clothes. The authorities checked the tombs in the cemetery to see if the cement had cracked. They found that the burial grounds smelled of dry pine needles. The women soon learned to place small pouches of the needles among their clothes, and with the arrival of winter, the smell of death abated. But when the ice melted in early March, the odor once more became unbearable. Holding bouquets of dried basil leaves to their noses after searching for nine days and nine nights, the children of Sheshi were able to trace the foul odor to

Grandmother Luza's house. She lived at the lower end of the village, where the houses themselves moved with the earth during the rainy season. The children found Uncle Kanjiki sitting as close as he could to the fireplace burning an olive log. It was then that the children learned of war and of the odor of death that it leaves behind. "I saw people piled up together like piles of dead leaves," he told them. "The young recruits picked the bodies up with a big shovel, almost ten thousand of them, and threw them into deep pits raging with fire. The smell infested our skin deeply; it even got into our blood. You can smell it, but I can feel it night and day. It is inside of me, nestling in every pore of my skin."

From that day on, every young man in Sheshi vowed never to go to war. Everyone in the village expected Uncle Kanjiki to die before the end of the grape harvest, but, as things turned out, he actually outlived everyone of his generation and the next. Oddly, I had never smelled death in the old librarian, even when we had sat close to one another looking for news about the faceless victim on the iron railing. Years later, I learned from a note he had written at the end of a page from a book he had read that the odor of death can only be snuffed out by blue violets. "It is the only flower capable of concealing the smell of death with the blue of the sky," he had written in a deep, red color.

At home, death arrived unannounced one winter day. It must have been a Friday, for the loneliness of the day could be felt in everything that I could behold. All stood still that morning. The sky was a tapestry of dark clouds partially hiding from view the tenement houses along Jackson Avenue. The termites had stopped gnawing the inside of the furniture. Mother suddenly regained the strength of her youth and arose from her chair. Her cheeks were full and flushed, and her forehead, clear of its maze of wrinkles, shone like those early morning rays which work their way from branch to branch, awakening the earth from its nightly torpor. With gestures reminiscent of those she used years ago in our one-room home in Sheshi overlooking the main square where the fountain leaned against the fig tree, Mother went about the ritual of preparing the morning coffee, taking the same degree of care as a priest might use in celebrating Mass. Time had ceased to be as we all sat at the table covered in white linen and set with the best china and silverware. This was the last cup of coffee we ever had together.

The snow on Jackson Avenue had turned into ice. Mother rose from her chair and walked slowly to her room, where she lay down upon the long bed. Father remained seated, following the flight of birds from tree-top to tree-top, unaware of what was taking place. Without saying a word or meeting Father's gaze, Sister began to return things to their rightful places.

I reached the church only to find the main door padlocked with a heavy chain. At the window of the one-story parish house, a light gleamed ineffectually. I rang the bell on the iron railing. As the clouds, as dark as night, loomed threateningly overhead, I thought of the long journey we had taken from the train station of Sheshi to Jackson Avenue. "Do not look back at the village," she had cautioned as we took our seats in the empty car. Little had I known that she herself was taking the town with her to the land across the ocean.

The priest, his eyes blood-shot and his body wrapped in a checkered woolen blanket, opened the window and wearily inquired what I wanted at that hour of the day. Regarding my countenance more closely, however, he relented, saying, "I'll be there in half an hour. I just have to put on some warm clothing to protect myself from the asthma."

The next day the clouds appeared to be even darker, and the warmer air produced an incessant drizzle. The few people who accompanied us at a distance uttered no words. At the gate, protected by a wide, dark umbrella, the old librarian stood motionless behind the pine tree, but he shook my hand when I approached him. He regarded my sister, who had aged precipitously, walk slowly with the rest of the family toward the main exit of the cemetery as he added, "I was told by the storekeeper on Jackson Avenue of the death in your family." He had started to walk away when he said, "The killing of the man on the railing of Saint Mary's Park never took place." The confidence with which he spoke left me speechless. "I will be going away as far as I can. I have been walking ever since the day the soldiers opened the gates of the halls of death."

The librarian appeared to be even more frail and beset by fear than when I had last seen him peering though his spectacles. As I observed him, I noticed how the dark clouds had dug deeper into the emptiness of the cemetery. Things had certainly come to an end, and there had been no time to even witness the changes. I leaned against the iron gate, a feeling of impotence triggering a dry sensation of nausea within me. A deeply-rooted loneliness blocked all the exits from the cemetery. The dark sky has nestled onto the tree tops, already bent by the constant drizzle.

The outline of the old librarian had melted in the distance. I thought of the underground bar in Harlem and the tapping curved fingers on the counter. The lonely figure of my sister floating on the thick fog appeared to rest on the window sill of the apartment. She had resumed the long wait for her suitor. This day was to change the course of many things. Suddenly I had become the anchor for my sister and for my younger brother, who had enclosed himself in the world of childhood, determined never to emerge.

The rains of the last days of the month gave way to more frequent snowstorms. Along the avenue leading to the elevated subway, which was held up by steel pillars that bisected the lower half of the city, the stores were decorated with the usual Christmas lights. The glitter followed the footsteps of the throngs of people moving from place to place. But the festive mood stayed clear of our house. Tired of the furtive glances of passersby, my sister had drawn the shades over the front window and enclosed the memories of our recent loss within the walls of our home.

Sister had replaced Mother in every way. Even her tone of voice had assumed that of Mother. She, too, was determined, in her own enigmatic way, to turn the clock back. Having found all the memorabilia from the village which Mother had hidden in the cedar chest, she now proceeded to fill every open space in the apartment with them. "Mother saved these things for us so that we could keep her image alive." The bureau scarves and antimacassars which Mother had sewn covered every conceivable surface. Their every stitch spoke of the hundreds of people who had left Sheshi for work in distant lands and of the trail of unseen tears that followed them. I had promised myself to break the silences of those lives stitched together in so many colors, for I knew that my mother would be feeling my presence even now, just as she always had in the hours before I would return home. More than once I had actually felt her thoughts mingling with mine as if to guide me or to relieve me of unidentifiable pressures working in the bottomless intricacies of my mind. "When God sends for me, your sister will watch over you and the rest of the family," she had said in moments of uncertainty during the rainy days of November.

I stopped at the corner of Jackson Avenue and gazed at

the dilapidated tenement buildings. The fire escapes were the only things still intact, although their black paint had dissolved into dark brown rust. The buildings were half empty, their windows broken, their ceilings charred. On the avenue, the well-lit stores filled with holiday colors and gifts belied the bleak air of the surroundings. Soon, as always seemed to be the case, the buildings would be torn down, reduced to yet another pile of debris. The memories of their former inhabitants would be suffocated in a mountain of dust, loaded into trucks and ferried away to fill an empty space or to clog underground canals at the city's edges, where the river formed a tight collar. I studied the steady flow of people, all driven by a restless urge to reach their invisible destination.

The noise of the river, swollen by recent rains, faded into the depths of the city. The underground music traversed endless cotton fields and marsh lands to feed the blood of wounds that would not heal. Here, faces as pale as the fake snow piled in the store windows, moved stiffly forward as if they belonged to an army of wooden soldiers. The cold air had solidified in the tree tops, gently bending the branches toward the streetlights. In the dark tunnels of the subway lines, the homeless took refuge while, above them, mothers dragged reluctant children past the moving angels and Santa Clauses who bowed repeatedly.

Here, too, along the broad avenue, countless signs announced the imminent demolition of abandoned buildings. The conversations which had taken place on the front stoops were a thing of the past. Not long before closing the shop, Father had confessed to Mother his difficulties in finding our own home. "Just the other day, I went out to buy milk because of the bad weather, but when I got back I could not find any of the signs that usually indicate the way. The loneliness I saw in the faces of the people was such as I had never seen before. It is a dreadful look that gnaws into your bones." Mother had shown no response.

The letter from Sheshi which announced the return of a relative to the village from the lands of the Orinoco coincided with the arrival of the Arctic winds. His father, Mother's youngest brother, had waited until his very last breath to see his son safely back home, but it was not to be. He died with his eyes open. In the last letter he sent to us, my uncle had written, "My son could not find his way out of the thick woods. The river he called the Orinoco had become an ocean trapping everyone." As the cold, made more biting by the whipping wind, chilled me, I recalled the face of my uncle, whom others called "the good man." He was the sort who would utter "Good evening" to the old women seated on stone benches outside their homes whispering to one another. "May the Virgin Mary keep you company."

My uncle's gentle, searching voice had a musical tone that moved to tears all who heard it. "He is truly an angel sent to us." No explanation was ever found for the feeling of emptiness his voice left in its wake. Each late afternoon the women sat outside their homes waiting for Uncle Kanjiki to pass on his way to the train station. Wearing a smile like that of an infant clinging to the mother with whom it has shared a world for nine months, he climbed the hill, convinced that his son would be arriving on the five o'clock train.

"My son will be coming from the big city where the wheat plays in the fields with the red poppies as they pursue the breezes from the blue sea." At the train station, Uncle Kanjiki waited patiently, straining to hear the locomotive emerging from the tunnel. As soon as he heard an approaching train, he sprang to his feet and advanced quickly toward the passengers, some of whom had alighted in error. Among these were others who, back in Sheshi after so many years, were both confused and virtually unrecognizable. These, he pitied.

But most of the time, no one got off the train, and the station remained, as usual, all but abandoned. Nonetheless, Uncle Kanjiki was not disconcerted by his son's failure to descend the rubber steps. "The eight o'clock train will be pulling in just a few hours from now," he mused. Later, full of smiles, his eyes bright, his ears alert, he hovered near the tunnel. This ritual was repeated until the last scheduled train arrived late at night. Then, someone would come to the station to fetch him home, where, after a night's rest, he would arise to resume the ceremony.

One morning, Uncle Kanjiki awoke before sunrise, as had been his custom ever since he had served as a soldier in the trenches of the snowy mountains. However, on that particular morning it was soon evident that a high fever had invaded his body. The hallucinations returned ...those that brought back images of soldiers exchanging greetings and news from their respective countries right before attempting to kill one another. The high fever kept Uncle Kanjiki at home; that is where the devoted friend who escorted him from the train station every night found him, unconscious, his legs swollen. Even so, Uncle Kanjiki had managed to pull on his boots, which were as shiny as they had been on the day of his return to Sheshi. It was an event the town had never forgotten.

It was spring, and the people of Sheshi were taking the icon of the Virgin of Constantinople in a procession from the chapel to the main church. The sacristan, unaware that all activity had stopped, continued to ring the church bells, but everyone else was looking at the soldier with the long beard and the skeletal face with deeply sunken, frightened eyes. No one in the front of the procession had recognized him except for a woman dressed in black, an old aunt on his mother's side. She grasped his hand and they walked home together without saying a word. Hundreds of eyes accompanied them from behind the curtains and doors left ajar. His mother, inside the one-room home with its small, round window broken through the thick stone wall over the door, had already started the fire with the dry olive logs she had kept since the year he had left. As his aunt left with the words, "I'll go and bring your wife and children here," his mother and her sister-in-law seated him gently on the wooden chair next to the fireplace. No sooner had Uncle Kanjiki felt the warmth of the woolen blanket placed over his knees than he fell asleep. In his mind, he was trying to remember each of his children, starting with the youngest, who had been barely able to stand the day he had left for the front. He could not recall his wife at all. Fear, caused by the dread which the piercing explosions had imprinted in his brain, had erased the image of his life-long companion. The children, however, always came to him during the cold nights as he kept watch over the icy landscape. He would play and roll over in the thin air with them until the early morning hours when the next soldier came to relieve him. Helped by the others, he would be set next to the burning logs of an open fire and given a hot cup of coffee. The bitter brew brought him back to the harshness of the cold and the depth of the fear which had settled over everyone in the trenches.

One night the soldiers on the other side of the icy field began to yell and promptly launched an attack. My uncle was left behind, taken for dead. When or how the battle had evolved, he could not remember. He awoke in a military hospital, unable to move half of his body. The war had already come to an end and an armistice had been signed in a red caboose when the killing between the soldiers in the two facing trenches began. No one of the dispatches reached the soldiers, whose position was unlisted on the war maps. The war ended as it had begun, although, perhaps, with more anger. Unable to find their way back home, endless lines of soldiers sat down in the road and waited for the sun to rise from behind the horizon. They covered their tired legs with the blankets the army had given them to take home. It was wrapped with one of those blankets, dark blue in color, that Uncle Kanjiki reached Sheshi after months of forgetfulness. All he could remember was the name of the village half asleep at the foot of the seven mountains, but the train master had no trouble locating it on his old map. "It is the last stop on the line that comes from the narrow sea."

Now Uncle Kanjiki's wife appeared at the house. Nothing stirred inside of him. He did not even recognize her voice. "He is not my husband," she announced abruptly. At that, his mother's eyes filled with tears, which she tried to contain, lest her son notice them. In fact, she was the only one who was completely certain of his identity. Even the aunt who had caught sight of him approaching the procession had acted more on instinct than conviction. "The war can really change people," his mother declared firmly. But the grave look she directed at her daughter-in-law did little to dissuade the younger woman, who took her leave with a bit of unwelcome advice: "You should notify the authorities so that they can help this poor soul regain his mind."

Her husband had inclined his head towards the fire, seeing only the image of the hospital and recalling his futile attempts all day long to move his legs. On the other side of the fireplace his mother and aunt sat scrutinizing his features to see if they fell into the proper alignment. Each, unaware of the other's efforts, went back in time to relive the three full days of torment that had preceded his birth. They hoped to see in his face now the full autumn moon that had been so red as to convince every frightened villager that an archangel had been born in their midst. But the soldier sat unmoved, almost hiding under the blanket, his head resting on his knees as the two women recalled how everyone in the village had burned dried oregano to ward off the dark fumes that descended from the red moon.

The mother, Luza, relived every detail of the birth, retracing every feature of her son from the moment the creature was shown to her. In the briefest of moments, she traversed the road of his time. She looked at him now, helpless and beaten, as if unable to fend off the snake in the bloody pond which was pulling him down, exhausting and drowning him. She was determined to stand there until that snake would have to come up for air. Then, she would attract him with her milk and free her son. She sat facing the tired and forlorn body of the soldier whose impenetrable mind might remain closed to her forever. At that very instant she began to assume the imposing figure of her great-grandmother Faela as the forgotten shape of the great serpent in the cave underneath the village began to stir in the deep silence of the home. The mother glanced fixedly into the flames burning chestnut wood. She waited patiently for the sizzling of the snake as it emerged from the fireplace, intent upon not confusing the sound with that of the burning cinders being pulled up by the cold air of the stone chimney.

Still, it wasn't long before the mother herself gave in to the sleep-inducing warmth. She saw a long procession of women, dressed all in black, with their heads bent and their hair disheveled, moving towards the cave of the sacred serpent. She felt her youth condensing in the deepest part of her womb. She followed the wailing cortège at a distance, gripped by an uncertain pain around her waist that grew as the dark silhouettes drew closer to the cave. The olive groves on each side of the dirt road shone as clearly as the full moon at the sky's zenith. Suddenly she felt a familiar touch on her back. It was her great-grandmother Faela, recognizable by the endless wrinkles on her forehead. She felt safe.

"I was waiting for you to come and join us," her great-grandmother whispered. Her voice, once soft, had become as rough as that of her great-grandfather, Tuci. Now she followed Faela, holding onto her skirt as the pain in her navel increased steadily. The procession reached the inside of the cave by following the flow of the winding brook. There the women washed their faces with the water dripping from the porous walls of the ancient cave. Then they uttered indecipherable incantations to the snake that twirled and raised its head, sending piercing sounds to the hundreds of beaming eyes reflected in the inner pool at the center of the cave. The great-grandmother, her face fierce, held the young girl by the waist, removed her clothes swiftly and dipped her into the center pool. The serpent swam straight forward, attracted by the shadow of the young girl, who trembled with fear as her great-grandmother let go of her. She felt a gentle pain, unlike any other, that made her quiver as tiny drops of blood rolled down her thighs into the water. The sight caused the women to howl lamentations. It was then that Faela gave her great-granddaughter the red-stained cloth, neatly folded into the shape of a poppy. "Go home and hide this cloth deep in the earth between the two ancient olive trees in the meadow between the village and the cemetery," she instructed.

The stars had begun to fade away, chased from the sky

by the rays of the sun, when Luza reached the road of the four crosses where her mother, Faela, waited in silence. Together they climbed the steep ravine that led to the first stone road of Sheshi. The white adobe houses of the oldest part of the village were reddened by the early lights of dawn piercing through the tall pine trees of the seven mountains. On their way to the square of the fountain, the mother and daughter encountered a line of people loading their beasts of burden for an early start upon work in the wheat fields. Unperturbed by the two women who walked as if burdened by the weight of time, the men continued to load their beasts. "May you walk with God," said Faela to the one who kept the best fields in the village. "May you return with the mother of Christ," answered the red-faced Roshi, who the people of Sheshi thought of as a man with the hands of Saint Joseph.

The sun turned bright yellow on the door of their home, warming the stone seat where the figs were set to dry for the winter. Faela had waited with a trembling heart the return of her daughter. Inside the house, she quickly returned to her own self, although with some anxiety. Her daughter Luza had matured into a complete woman. "From now on," Faela told her in a surprisingly submissive voice, "you shall open and close the door to our home. I have polished the key with vinegar and placed it in the opening above the fireplace." That was the last time her mother had spoken to her.

As Luza opened her eyes and the cinders turned into ashes in the fireplace, she saw that the blue patches under her son's eyes were now completely dark. The uniform he wore still had deep tears. "I shall mend it," she said to herself, "so that the people of Sheshi can see the colors of war and the cries of death in the copper buttons."

Luza rose from the wicker chair she herself had woven as two drops of blood fell onto the stone base of the fireplace.

When she took the wooden pail and placed some hot ashes on them, their odor awakened in her son the arduous road of return still in his eyes. Kanjiki was painfully aware of the long nights in the trenches with the rains and the deep mud that reached up to his knees, paralyzing him more than the fear of a stray bullet coming from the enemy's lines just two hundred yards ahead. The days had been long and the nights even longer. He remembered clearly the words the soldiers exchanged with one another. "Can you tell me why it is easier to die than to kill?" The soldiers had all become brothers in the face of so much suffering.

Kanjiki moved closer to the fireplace. The guilt of not having resisted those soldiers who had come to get him that late afternoon as he was returning home after clearing the undergrowth from the olive trees had never left him. Night after night he relived the helpless image of his wife as they forced him inside the carriage with the other recruits. The children, oblivious, had been following a long column of ants busily taking their provisions down the hole the youngsters had found when they turned over a pile of leaves. "I did not even have time to say good-bye to them." The people of Sheshi had come out of their homes to see Kanjiki being taken to the train station in a single file with twenty others from the village. "I felt the guilt grow inside of me as the bell on the wall of the train station announced the arrival of the train."

Now Luza brought her son a cup of hot tea prepared with dry poppy seeds. The familiar taste dispelled the feeling of rejection he had seen in his wife's gray eyes. Luza drew the woolen blanket up to his neck and crossed his forehead three times, reciting ancient orations that she had learned on the nights before the birth of Jesus, the One who understood all things.

Henceforth, Kanjiki slept for many nights and many days. When he finally awoke, he asked his mother for his wife and children. Luza hesitated, pretending to gather more wood for the fireplace. "I want to be taken home," her son said in a more determined tone.

"Your wife did not come to see you when your aunt brought you down from the main square," Luza replied, with the understanding of a mother sharing the grief of her child. He remained stupefied, not knowing what to make of her words, but he managed to get up from the wooden seat with some difficulty and to assert decisively, "I will go home now!"

Realizing his resolve, Luza offered to walk down the road with him. Kanjiki could not remember the way home, even though he had walked it so many times, for his own house had once belonged to his paternal grandfather. The one-story house was known to everyone in Sheshi because of the pomegranate tree which inebriated the whole village with its odor when it bloomed in the early spring. Not a door opened as mother and son descended the narrow street. "Where is everyone?" Kanjiki mumbled to his mother as he clutched her arm, feeling weaker with every step he took. "Many have moved up North to search for work; they just locked their doors and took the keys with them, not saying whether they were coming back one day. The war was too long and, with the men gone, the wives could not have the children starve."

Things were beginning to make sense to him. With some trepidation, he lowered his eyes, noting how an inexplicable sense of foreboding accompanied the urge to see his children. As they approached the fountain of the sweet waters, Kanjiki recognized the house with the two nooks on each side of the door. Wild oregano had grown all over the front of the house, and the chestnut door was weather beaten, its bottom almost totally warped. The house was steeped in an air of loneliness, sadness written all over its face. As Kanjiki saw that there were no children playing in front of the house, he knew that there was no one inside. "Where have they gone?" he inquired sadly.

"Your wife did not recognize you and, out of fear, took the two youngest to her mother's village. The oldest has gone to a place he calls 'the mountain of paradise'...at least, that is what he wrote in the only letter he has sent since his departure. He could not wait to leave after he searched for you for months through the mountains of perennial snow. I cannot forget the night he returned, announcing so assuredly that you would never come back. He told everyone in the village that he had seen enough dead to fill a train that would stretch from our station to the city of the glittering waters. He was determined not to end like one of those soldiers with fear still in their eyes, piled on top of one another like discarded rags."

The sense of guilt Kanjiki felt now had begun to open a deep wound in his chest. "I think it's best that we return home. I will give her time to come back when she feels the need to. As for my son, I shall be waiting for his return starting tomorrow." He made this vow unwittingly, not realizing that the long wait for his son was to become his agony and that he would close his eyes without ever closing the wound gnawing at his chest. But as the night is followed by the day, Kanjiki never lost hope. It gave him the strength in the long hot days of summer and the short cold days of winter to scale the hill to the train station.

Luza never attempted to dissuade her son from his ritual; instead, she ended up believing in his dream as much as he did. Morning after morning she would awaken him at exactly the same time, not one minute before nor one minute after. Together they drank the cup of dark coffee sweetened with one spoonful of sugar she made from her own beets and then they walked half-way to the train station. The mother waved to her son before she entered the Church of the Dead on top of the hill to begin her prayers, which lasted until the sun brightened the whole interior of the church.

The clock on Sheshi's town hall tower was running far ahead of Luza. She barely heard the tolling which for so many years had corresponded to the kind of work she was to undertake. From the old fountain in the main square, the elders followed the daily footsteps of Luza and her son. For the mother and son, time stood still. They aged unaware of the process. Sheshi had also begun to change quickly. The young and the old no longer strolled freely back and forth in the square, and the topics of discussion, when they did take place, referred to faraway places that only a few could identify.

And so it was that the day came when a high fever invaded Kanjiki's whole body. He still managed to get out of bed that morning. He was more determined than ever, despite an uneasy premonition, to climb the steep hill to the train station and to sit in his usual place to wait for his son, counting every train that passed en route to the city of the frigid winds. Kanjiki's legs buckled as he rose from the bed, but, with his mother's help, he sat on the wooden bench next to the fireplace. Even though the logs were still burning brightly, he felt chilled deep in every bone as he drank the cup of coffee mixed with poppy seeds.

Luza noticed that the pallor in her son's face was being invaded relentlessly by blue patches. She had seen this change take place in people many times ever since her own mother had taken her to the neighbor's house to look upon a dying person. "It is best that you look death in the face," her mother had said when Luza was just six. She knew then that living was nothing else but preparing for that final moment, and everything was just a way of avoiding the constantly lurking shadows. "Poor child," she murmured, feeling an indolent pain deep in her chest. "He was destined never to build a bridge between his eyes and those of his son." With dry eyes, Luza washed her hands with water boiled with bay leaves and proceeded, with great effort, to place her son over a clean white sheet on her own bed. She scraped every speck of dust from his body and bathed him with holy water. She ironed his white shirt carefully and placed a tie around his neck to match the dark grey suit. He looked the way he had on the day he married the woman who, at that time, could see inside of him deeper than anyone else in the village.

Finding her black woolen shawl among her prized possessions, Luza folded it into a triangle and drew it over her head and mouth. The few people in the neighborhood who happened to be outside knew upon seeing her that death had lodged in Luza's home. By the time she returned there with the village priest, whom she had to awaken from his usual afternoon nap, the bells of the Church of the Dead were announcing the death of the returned soldier with their usual melancholy. The sound pierced the townspeople's hearts and filled them with trepidation. The priest, mumbling prayers from the small breviary that he kept inside the front pocket of his black tunic, sprinkled holy water over the body stretched out upon the sparkling white sheet. He was taken by the serene smile that had settled over the face of the dead soldier; it was a smile that he was not to forget for years to come. At times, especially when awakening from his nap, he wondered if that smile were not, indeed, an indication of the promised life that the Church fathers had spoken and written about in so many languages.

Kanjiki's wife learned of his death the next day, but she was not among the long procession of women dressed in black who accompanied the casket half way towards the road that led to the cemetery. At the chapel under the mountain, they placed a wreath on each of the three wooden crosses. Then only the men carried the casket to the small chapel in the cemetery. There it lay for three full days with relatives taking turns watching over it for any signs of life that might have been overlooked. My Uncle Kanjiki was buried in the family lot with all his kin of years past, and with them he would watch over the others as they waited for their turn to dive into the blue pool of water.

On her return to the village after the third day, Luza was certain that the dark figure with the black shawl over her face was that of her daughter-in-law. She cursed her for denying her son peace of mind before his death, and she vowed never to allow her into her home, knowing that her curses had never failed her. From then on, Luza remained dressed in black. For awhile, she tended her fields only when everyone else had left their own plots to return home, but soon after, she placed a lock on her door.

Years later, some distant relatives attempted to sell the house. No buyer came forward, for those who remembered anything of the terrible destiny of the wandering soldier did not dare violate the accursed space. Rumors spread quickly, especially fortified by those who shared the same neighborhood, that a mysterious person had been seen painting the front door and filling in the cracks between the stones in the front wall night after night. Others insisted that, as they prepared to go to the fields in the hours before sunrise, they would see a person seated on the front stone bench, his face buried in his hands. The laments he emitted awoke in everyone nearby a strong urge to cry. His piercing cries only stopped when the sun hit the front entrance of the house and dried the pool of water that formed there every morning. The letters my father received from Sheshi month after month never failed to mention those cries and that pool of water. "It is as blue as the sky, but no one dares to look into it." In time, the neighbors, unable to sleep, abandoned the surrounding homes, and the steps leading from Luza's house to the main square became impassable.

Sheshi was changing faster than at any previous time. "One of these days, no one will be able to return home," the elders grumbled as they strolled around the main square, placing one foot in front of the other with all the strength they could muster. The old-timers could see the changes more clearly than the young ones, who moved along freely but were unaware of what was taking place in the olive groves that lined the road leading to the train station.

The day the eldest son of the now almost forgotten dead soldier got off the five-thirty train, Sheshi was experiencing the hottest summer ever. The only living thing that accompanied him from the station down the hill and through the narrow streets that led to the house whose image he had reviewed every night before falling asleep on his front porch surrounded by palm trees was a limping black dog dragging his tail. Every door and window of the village was shut tight to thwart the heat and to mute the buzzing of the cicadas. He carried only a small suitcase with a few of his personal belongings. Among them was a photograph of the woman who had saved his life on the mighty river whose source was the great ocean of the Pacific waters. Whenever he looked at her image, he recalled the moment he awoke on the hammock tied between two palm trees and looked for the first time into her amber eyes, brightened even more by the white-washed houses around her. The breeze that day had been as soft as the one he remembered in Sheshi on the first day of spring. He was destined to relive that moment... sometimes with others, but mostly alone.... for the rest of his life as the sun began to hide behind the seven mountains.

"It all began with the sky blackening and the wind toppling trees. Two of my friends and I had decided to take the boat down the Orinoco River and join thousands of others in search of gold in the ravines of the green mountains. It was a damp, foggy morning. The sun was blocked by dark clouds that carried the smell of burning trees. The boat, carried along by a swift current, crashed against the many tree trunks floating in the river. The fog prevented us from seeing each other as the slimy air and the penetrating sounds of the jungle added to our fear and confusion. The three of us said nothing as the waters grew murkier. We lashed ourselves to the center seat of the boat to avoid tumbling over if we fell asleep. The night rushed by. The next morning, the sun's rays revealed a mountain riddled by thousands of caves and overrun by prospectors who, as so many ants, dug furiously as they held onto long ropes running from the bottom to the top of the mountain. The sky darkened quickly and the heavy rains that followed forced us to take to higher ground. It was in the heart of the jungle that we became separated. I heard my companions' screams, but I could not locate them. I cannot say how long I walked until she found me. I felt my body heavy with leeches. I was being sucked in by the force of the jungle, a power unlike any other. It was the woman in this photograph, always so quiet, who saved me from the blood suckers. I can still smell the odor of the burning leaves that cleared my mind of the sounds of the deep woods. She was a good woman. I can still hear the wind blowing through her hair and see the clear waters of the river mirroring in her eyes. But her face in the photograph does not say anything.

She knows I had to come back to see my father. I learned that the war had ended from an old newspaper blown to my feet as I watched the dolphins with the breasts of a woman feed their young. Of Sheshi I remembered clearly the train station and the road to the left that led to the next village inhabited by dark, curly-haired people who looked so much alike that no one was able to tell them apart. They used to say that, at night, everyone in that village turned into a crow, feeding on the carcasses of dead animals."

Kanjiki's son, Zini, looked about and took stock. Gone were the trees with the white flowers that used to line that road to the next village. They had been usurped by tall buildings with front and back balconies. The water fountain only dripped intermittently now, the few drops of water drying upon the burning basin. Down below, the old part of Sheshi, choked with sunlight, appeared abandoned. Wild weeds had invaded the cracks between the stones because the streets had been empty of playing children for years. The hunting sparrows no longer chased butterflies among the fig leaves. Zini could do no more than sense the presence of the old women who hid behind the doors to their homes, frightened by the presence of the young men who returned to the village with strange ways.

Zini recognized his great-aunt's house, its grounds now invaded by the prickly "drizët" that at one time had only grown around the entrance to the sacred cave. He recalled his great aunt's words, "I always leave the door open so that the house can breathe." Now the door was shut tightly, tented in a canopy of spider webs.

Zini recognized the chiseled volcanic stones his great-uncle Selimi has shaped like soft twigs, hiding in them the thirst of his imagination. There had not been a father in Sheshi who did not wish to have one of his sons become an apprentice to Selimi, but he had refused to comply. "It is not something that anyone can learn. I myself do not know what guides my fingers to work that stone." At first that answer was taken as a sign of arrogance by those in the village, but, with the passing of time, they began to recognize that there was some truth in what Selimi said. His own children were unable to do what their father did. The seat by the side entrance to the house still shone as it had the day Selimi had announced his work was finished. Soon after, his fingers became wracked with pain and misshapen. He salved them with a cream his wife made from the soft bark of a licorice root and kept them inside woolen gloves. In no time, Selimi's head began to grow visibly larger. To those who wanted to know why his skull was expanding, he answered that it was because he could no longer let out the images that were begging to escape. He became all head, until the musty afternoon when he choked to death. When his wife found the glass of water untouched, she knew her husband was no longer with her. She found the first three letters of her name scribbled on the front table where he rested his curved fingers.

Later in the day, as he returned to the main square, Zini learned that it had been his great-aunt who had accompanied his father to his grandmother's house. At the café they confirmed that she had guided his father home, disoriented as he was. "The conductor who helped your father get off the train said he remembered the name of the train station only when a lone passenger standing in front of the exit uttered the name 'Sheshi.' It was Besniki returning home from his chestnut grove. He carried Kanjiki on his shoulders half way to the main square. Your father carried such a heavy burden that not even the station master identified him."

"The village seems half deserted, although I can sense

the hidden eyes behind the doors scrutinizing every move that I make. The woman silently follows me just a few paces behind. An oppressive air emanates from the white-washed homes on both sides of the narrow street. There is fear lurking behind the closed windows. It must be like the cold shudder I felt when I opened my eyes after the rains in the thickness of the jungle. The sounds of the unseen lasted for days. A hand guided me through the main street of the village. Pile dwellings soaked in water. The silence ended when the plants absorbed every drop of water."

"There is no one living here," said the woman who followed behind Zini. The many steps that ended in the font of the house, at one time filled with flowers that smelled of early dawn, were no longer there. The rains of the past years had deposited a sea of granite pebbles. Zini sat on the broken stone seat that stood on the side of Benjamini's house. Even the cats were gone. "I knew then that my father was dead and the house had been abandoned." Never again would anyone live inside Kanjiki's house. It had been given to him by his father on his wedding day.

"Keep it well," he had admonished. "It has been in our family for as long as I can remember. The memories inside will never allow a stranger to inhabit it."

The heat of the afternoon had already hidden beneath the red roof tiles. Zini recalled waiting patiently, as a young boy, for his father to return home from the fields. One day his father had brought back the nest of a rare blue bird. "It sings like the angels in church on Sunday," he had confided.

Zini thought, "I helped the blue bird grow its feathers and then I let it go on top of the fig tree down the ravine." That had been the last time that the people of Sheshi had seen Kanjiki's son. He had taken with him the memories of his home and the sound of the cicadas in the heat of the day.

What Zini would never be able to forget was the callousness with which his father's mother had received him. "You killed your father more than the war in that forsaken land," Luza had said. Those words gnawed at Zini for the rest of his life. "Have the decency, at least," she had added with an even sterner scowl, "to visit his grave on the east side of the cemetery next to the pine tree with the darkest bark."

"I knew exactly the place she indicated. As children we used to hide behind that trunk convinced that it warded off the souls who wandered without finding a place to rest. From the hills watching the sun turn pale orange, we followed the slow movement of the caravan of peasants returning to Sheshi from the fields, much as their ancestors had done throughout the centuries." Zini returned to his grandmother's house, but he found it closed. The toothless woman who had followed him since his arrival came up to say that it was the time that Luza prayed in the Church of the Dead. "She never misses a day."

Zini took the road that led to the train station, where he waited for the five o'clock train. "I can still feel the cold wind descending from the mountain as I waited for that train. It was a punishing wind that made my teeth chatter. I looked around and felt the silence nestling on top of the chestnut trees. I would have given anything to have said good-bye to my grandmother. It also became clear that I would never come back to the place where I first began to look for ways to catch those butterflies that filled the people of Sheshi with dreams and forced them to leave their homes." The sun was rapidly setting behind the seven mountains. The lines of people waiting to embark in the city of the sea were no longer there. Zini spent the remaining days of his life in the land of the palm trees and endless sunshine, measuring time by the heights of the waves and the songs of the gulls surfing between the sky and the ocean.

The snow was still coming down as I moved along with them, inching toward the main avenue. The lights on Southern Boulevard were fewer and unsteady as a lazy army of snowflakes fell over them. Jackson Avenue was completely deserted. The electric lines had been snatched from the cables. The silence that reigned in the tenement houses was broken now and then by the rustling of the rats going through the garbage cans. The sharp fingernails of the cold night scraped incessantly upon the cement between the bricks. In the house, my sister was sitting motionless, her fingers crossed over her black dress. "How could you have stayed away from home on the day we buried our dead?" she challenged. Inside the house everything was in order, dusted and polished. The next morning would bring a new beginning.

I spent the night making and remaking the image of Uncle Kanjiki and the futile waiting for his son, Zini, to return home from the place he never located on any map of the world. In a way, we are all waiting for that one encounter that will open the door that allows us to see the space where the eyes see no light and the hands lose their sense of touch and emptiness is all around, painless. From afar, throngs of people seek refuge in their automobiles moving among the shadows of the neon lights darkening the fading colors of distant skies. Others, many others, place their antennae eyes inside the glass cubicles filled with objects that enslave their desires like childhood toys. Still others labor late at night when the dilapidated buildings, crowned with corroded fire escapes, rule the night with their silent guns. The clouds dive incessantly into the murky waters of the East River. The house numbers move from place to place, enslaving those who fall into the quicksand of the shoreline. Abortive screams leave no trail of their bloody prisons.

Winter had finally been swept away by the soft winds of spring streaming in from where the sun sets in the late afternoon on the tallest hill of Saint Mary's Park. Our tenement home was the only one left standing on Jackson Avenue. Around it, half-standing in a welter of scattered bricks, were derelict structures, their roofs caved in. The different faces and voices that had inhabited the steps of those former homes had vanished. Gone also were the Sunday visits of my father's few remaining acquaintances. The closing of the barber shop had brought everything to an end.

Sister, still dressed in black, had taken charge of preserving the memories of our home. The memorabilia, cleaned and dusted daily, remained where it had been placed on the day Mother, my younger brother Darius and I had arrived. "This is your new home," my father had exulted as he opened the door. Mother had tried in vain to fill the apartment with the memories of the old house in Sheshi. As years went by, what had been left behind managed to take complete control of the new. Sister was determined to fight the ravages of time. She rarely went out and on the door she placed a second lock; indeed, she showed no interest at all in the world outside. She echoed Mother even in her choice of words. Slowly the home turned into a world in itself and became estranged to its surroundings.

I returned to school but I no longer walked over the bridge that connected the two boroughs of the city. The days succeeded one another in their usual routine. "Your coffee is ready," Sister would announce in the morning as she reached for the cup, cleaned it and placed it on one end of the table. The simmering coffee pot filled the kitchen with a familiar aroma that silenced the ticking of the clock on top of the gas stove. For herself, she would take the blue-flowered cup brought from Sheshi, wipe it with a damp cloth, fill it half way with coffee and, with an utterly natural air, take her place next to the window. It was a morning ritual carried on daily from season to season. "I left the white shirt on your bed. It is freshly ironed," she would add without taking her glance from the window.

The city bus on the avenue was rarely full. It went through different neighborhoods, each clearly marked by colors and the canopies on the windows before it reached the bridge. The street signs carried the names of people each neighborhood venerated. A crowd of young men played handball against a front brick wall. The sidewalk was a maze of disharmonious sounds, and at each window trembling hands grasped the iron bars. Against this backdrop of brown and gray and perforated bricks, the passersby moved unevenly to the beat of a saxophone coming from the underground. The city bus moved along, stopping only when a potential passenger hailed it. On each side of the road, grayish eyes watched, filled with memories of past voyages from the river of sweat to the drowning waves of the high seas. One saw row after row of impenetrable faces.

The street below the station was littered with soda bottles, and a stagnant air made its way into the alleys between the tenements. Not a light could be seen in any of the homes set on this canvas of private depths weaving indifference. Yet, 506 Jackson Avenue shone brightly into the mirror of the lamppost, although the steps to its entrance, like all the others on that block, evinced no memories of past years. The stoniness of the air had even turned the few trees that lined the street into sculptured icicles.

Sunday came full of promises. The people on the

avenue, dressed in their best apparel, waited patiently for a cloudless sky so that they might talk over the events of the week with someone else. Others wandered through the main path of Saint Mary's Park until they found their eyes fixed on the swings full of children sharing flight with the black crows above. The day came to an end when the last beam of sunlight faded into the spreading night. In just six days, the ritual began again with only a few inconsequential variants that posed no threat to the only day of the week in which time and memories embraced as they waited for the first days of the coming season. The days and the months that followed unperceived by anyone gnawed fervently at past memories like the waves of a stormy day crashing against the shores and leaving behind bits of orphaned shells.

Chapter Eight

The monthly letters from Sheshi had ceased to reach the house on Jackson Avenue. The bridge that brought together the depths of the sacred cave and the dreamless reality of the tenement house had all but vanished. Each letter had been read aloud as we all gathered at the dinner table. Each had begun with the same revelation: "The swallows this year were fewer than in previous years." But the last letter had spoken of many a bad omen.

"Difficult times are awaiting us. Our boys have been leaving for the North like herds of sheep, and the fields are yielding only weeds. The women no longer sit outside their homes waiting for their men to return; some have been seen late at night howling like wolves in search of food. People swear to have seen these women change into unrecognizable beasts rushing wildly toward the entrance to the sacred cave. Each door is locked with the arrival of the first dark streaks of the night. The elders have been saying that this year's wine will turn into vinegar, and that the oil from the dark olives will not shed its drops of water. The few women who attend Mass on Sunday have seen rats scurrying between the wooden benches. Prefti Vlasë no longer walks through the main square, and many have even forgotten what he looks like. The woman who cleans his house told her neighbors that the priest is awaiting the arrival of his sister from the road that sees the first rays of light. In a short while, no one will remember Sheshi the way our forefathers conceived it when they first arrived from the salty seas carrying on their shoulder the icon of the Virgin of Constantinople."

The one who remained at home more determined than ever to fight the ever-threatening changes assailing the neighborhood was Sister. Her nightly conversations with

Mother as she stared at the empty chair next to the kitchen window grew in frequency. She no longer looked at the lamppost as she had done for years. With iron conviction, she erased the image from her mind and placed a thick curtain on the window overlooking the street. Now she kept her own watch, dividing the day among the many chores she executed with the precision of the evening shade that never failed to come to the kitchen window. Only the streaks of white hair on each side of her head indicated the passing of time. The black dress she wore had become an intimate part of her as she assumed the semblance of Mother.

By this time, Darius, the youngest of the family, had breached the enclosed world of our sister. He had become an expert machinist, awed by the countless pieces that worked in unison inside a machine. The walls in his room were filled with mechanical designs connected to one another by alternating colors of red and black. "One of these days," he would say, "I will design a machine that breathes in contaminated air and exhales air as pure as that I used to inhale down the ravine in old Sheshi." This endeavor had become his obsession. At times he awakened during the night to add a line or two to the design. The room soon filled with pile upon pile of pictures of machines taken from all the magazines Darius could find. He devised his own mathematical formula for creating a certain harmony between the impure air, the steel pieces and the release of invisible energy. In his room, he spoke his own language, one that sounded like that which grandmother had spoken as we sat around her fireplace in the house on the lower edge of Sheshi.

The dedication and conviction in Darius' work left no room for questions. The years galloped by, leaving only traces of deep wrinkles in his forehead and an expression of sadness that he was never to shed. Mother had been the first to notice the hidden face of melancholy that he tried to bury among the mechanical designs. "Your brother was born on a sad day," she reminded Sister. "The road he has to traverse will not be a happy one. Keep an eye on him. Put signs in the corridors that will direct him home." As always, Mother had seen far more clearly than anyone else what lay ahead. Her power to visualize what was taking place in the present that would emerge in the future with uncanny accuracy shocked all the women on her grandmother's side of the family and inflicted much fear in everyone in Sheshi. "He has inherited the runaway imagination of your grandfather, and in this land, it will be his undoing."

It took Darius only a few months to rebel against the rigid school code which provided no answers to his questions. "Where you put me is not a place to keep busy. I cannot even turn my pen the way I want," he complained when he got home, fighting to hold back the tears that wanted to course freely down his cheeks. "The others don't know it, but the fierce eyes of the teachers intend to make us become silent sheep."

What Darius most missed were the unending wheat fields dancing in the wind and the wild oregano plants that carpeted the seven mountains at their lower level. His eyes waited to fetch every white cloud that floated by his accustomed place in front of our house. There, surrounded by four walls shattered by a stray bomb during the war, he had planted every seed he could find and waited for the wind to bring closer the cloud that would water them with a few drops of rain. "I hear a woman crying endlessly," he often confided to Mother, "just as the sun begins to hide behind the mountain."

Darius' seeds grew where once stood the one-room

house of the ageless widow who had been heard calling for her husband until her last breath. He had gone with his regiment to the far-distant fields of Russia. "He is only waiting for the snows to melt so that he can find the road back to the land that smells of violets," the widow told the people of Sheshi until they no longer believed her. The young in the square changed faces as the wooden benches decayed under the snows and rains of winter, but the widow never lost hope for the return of her husband. She gave Darius a pomegranate seed she had saved and kept warm inside a blue bottle which she kept on top of her fireplace. "Plant this seed in your garden," she directed, "and when it grows, you will tell my husband where to find me."

Darius had planted the seed the day she died. On that day, the widow had cleaned the house and had fed each of her domestic animals. The seed did not sprout until the first remains of the one hundred blue soldiers began to arrive at the train station of Sheshi. That was in early May. The day dawned with a cold breeze. The cold had delayed the blooming of the fruit trees by three weeks. In the village, no one had gone to the fields and the shops had been ordered closed by the Mayor. The square stood still. The water from the fountain seemed to flow noiselessly. The young and the old mingled with some strangers who had come from the nearby villages. They were all there to receive small boxes with the remains of the blue soldiers from the killing fields of the Russian steppes. The elderly women gathered on both sides of the fountain while the men, holding onto their canes, stood in silence in front of the café. All waited for the officials to begin the march towards the train station. They had been told that the boxes carried no names, only numbers, and that the bones were incomplete and intertwined with roots. "They are the bones of your sons, brothers and husbands, and so the grief is for all of us to share," exclaimed the Mayor, dressed in black for the occasion. Those were the only words he spoke.

Prefti Vlasë, touched by the events, awoke from his deep sleep to follow behind the tricolor flag carried by one of the soldiers. The balconies and windows were covered with black sheets. The men and women fell into line behind the town's officials.

A steady drizzle had begun to fall on the procession accompanied by patches of fog that had begun to descend from the seven mountains late in the morning. The line of mourners melted slowly in the gray mist of the heights. Someone in the procession had ventured to suggest delaying the digging of the graves until the earth softened a bit, but another, who barely kept pace with the rest, spoke against the delay. "Those bones have traveled too many miles to be waiting for burial. Their torture must end today."

In fact, the gathering of the remains at the train station lasted for months. Spring had departed with no memories left behind. The wheat fields filled with red poppies were not celebrated by anyone. It took all of the able-bodied of Sheshi to carry the one hundred boxes to the cemetery. The remains were distributed to the proper relatives according to the dreams they had had. Yet many of the boxes remained unclaimed. Photographs of the missing soldiers were placed on the remains with the hope of getting some response from the bits of bones, but to no avail. It was finally decided by Prefti Vlasë and the Mayor of Sheshi that only the very young should take the remaining boxes to the community burial ground. The next day, with all the adults behind closed doors and the young ones dressed in white, the procession to the cemetery began.

It took three days and three nights for the burning

candles to dispel the dark clouds filled with cries hovering over Sheshi. As for the smell of death emanating from the boxes already growing mushrooms from their fissures, it was never more to leave the village. It served as a constant reminder to the old and young of what awaited everyone. To those who had been fortunate enough to identify the remains, the odor caused unending hallucinations. Lines of ragged soldiers with missing limbs, their feet sinking in deep snow, not knowing which way to go and, perhaps, hoping for that stray bullet that would put an end to their misery, appeared whenever these relatives closed their eyes.

The most touching delusion was related by Prefti Vlasë during the usual Sunday sermon delivered to the few elderly women attending Mass. He swore as he lifted the Holy Eucharist that he had seen the Son of God wandering through the village's streets and knocking on every door in search of shelter. "He has come to us and we failed to recognize Him," Prefti Vlasë announced to the few faithful present. His powerful voice reached all those in the square and in the café, who moved closer to the Church of the Dead to listen to the fiery words of the priest. "He has come to deliver to us the bones of your husbands, brothers and sons and to remind us of the futility of all wars." What amazed the crowd in the square were not so much the delivery of the sermon but the changes they noticed in the prelate's face as he silently walked past them after Mass. Years later they would continue to swear that, on that day, they had seen the face of Christ on Prefti Vlasë. The radiant look in his eyes took them back to the sacred icons they had seen on the day of their first communion.

The smell of putrid air given off by the mushrooms that had been growing everywhere in Sheshi suddenly came to an end with the appearance of the first blue violets. The decayed mushrooms turned into a white powder quickly dispersed by the soft whistling winds coming from the north shore of Africa. Once again each family in Sheshi went back to its usual spring routine. Homes were turned inside out, flower vases were stripped of the winter mold, and the vegetable gardens were plowed and blanketed with compost. The girls busied themselves with their dowry, and the young men flocked to the main square dressed and perfumed with their best. The boxes with the remains of the dead soldiers were forgotten in the communal burial grounds as something that had happened beyond the realm of memories.

It was at this time that Darius had learned the secret of the seeds. He vowed not to share that knowledge with anyone who did not wish to remember the remains of those who had gone to the Great War and who had come back with only their bones inside the wooden boxes. The clock on the municipal building of Sheshi was playing its usual tricks without allowing the people to see the effect it was having on them when the town crier announced the first killing. It occurred in one of those narrow streets that seemed to have been forgotten by the young and old alike because they remained outside the main square and had the strange smell of old things. It was early spring, the people of Sheshi remembered. The cherry trees were in full bloom with so many flowers that not even the branches could hold them. At first, the promising flowers brought smiles to the elders who readied themselves to move to the stone seats outside their homes for storytelling. But, as the days went by, the flowers started to turn brighter than the rays of the sun at midday. The intense light blinded anyone who dared to look at the cherry trees. The nights had turned brighter than the days. For the young who needed to be close to their loved ones, the hours seemed like weeks and the weeks seemed like years. At night, the café quickly turned into an open confessional booth. The secrets of their beloved, so carefully stored in the arcane recesses of their minds for months and years, became public information.

That very night, Ramadin, Darius' best friend, had put on his best suit, saved for his future wedding to the girl with the greenest eyes of all the people in Sheshi. Those who saw him walk up the hill from the old square with the church of Shën Koli would never forget the cloud of cicadas passing over the village. The noise deafened all those who ventured outside their homes. The only one who remained impervious to the noise was Ramadin himself. His mind had already entered the blue house of Emira, aided by the candle flame in her front window.

Ramadin slowed his pace as he approached her house. He looked all around to make certain that no one else was present before stopping below Emira's window. The pounding of his heart produced a cold sweat that rushed from his forehead down his face. Taking out his embroidered handkerchief and slowly wiping the sweat from his eyes, Ramadin could see that the candle had gone out and the window pane had turned pitch dark. He quickened his pace, hoping to see Emira at the Fountain of the Three Roads where she usually went to fetch water for the evening meal. It was not to be. The fountain on that day had been shut down because of the low pressure from the reservoir on top of the train station.

The days that followed were the hottest ever felt in Sheshi. The cherry blossoms withered, leaving the branches scarred. The land quickly turned into a desert with deep crevices. The streets were empty of people. Here and there, stray dogs stretched out looking for coolness on the dark blue stones in the secluded alleys. Swarms of dark horseflies swirled around the bits of fresh garbage left outside the homes. Ramadin could not recall ever feeling such silence. It felt as if Sheshi had been emptied of people, leaving it to the mercy of the flies and ants.

"The air smelled as it had the day the men of the village, all in black uniforms, were taken to the train station by the Mayor. On that day I stayed at home taking care of the mule. I remember I had been told to change the bandage on the wound on the mule's knee every hour." Ramadin's father had told him to chop lard and add a bit of salt to it. It was the last time that Ramadin was to hear his father's voice. He had never dared to look at his father when he spoke to him.

That morning Ramadin sensed a strange feeling he could not pinpoint. A sensation of total calm had spread within him, leaving him utterly detached from his surroundings. Inexplicably, Ramadin decided to put on the suit and white shirt his mother had put away for when he decided to wed. He cleaned and polished the dark boots with a piece of charcoal from the fireplace. The pain he had felt deep in his belly button during the night had become more pronounced. He changed the pillow case from his sweat-soaked bed linens which smelled of the unrequited desire to be with Emira. The morning sun shone brightly as Ramadin walked on heavy legs toward the old square. Shën Koli stood between the shade and the blinding sunlight. The sun above the old square was a fireball of invisible clouds shooting down wave after wave of burning rays. He took out his embroidered white handkerchief and placed it around his neck, this time to protect his shirt collar from the sweat dripping down his cheeks. The window panes of Emira's room blinded his eyes. It must have been, by now, late in the afternoon when the sun shone the brightest. "I will wash my hands at the fountain and I will wait for the sun to go down," Ramadin resolved, not daring to show any sign of anxiety to whoever could be watching him from behind the doors.

Ramadin noticed that the fountain was going dry and that signs of corrosion had begun to appear around the metal tubing. "How could the fountain have deteriorated?" he wanted to ask, but the thought of Emira did not allow him to pursue that concern. The heat had turned the stone on the fountain into an oven. Intertwined rays in the shape of a halo had settled over the old church. The evaporating fumes from the walls of the houses had reduced the hanging begonias to dust. By now, Ramadin was having trouble breathing. As he struggled to catch a satisfyingly deep breath, he looked for a shady place from which to watch the seven mountains leaning on one another. He needed a place to sit, for his legs had become as heavy as the logs he carried down the mountains with his father.

The previous night Ramadin had dreamt that a tree trunk had fallen on his chest, crushing his lungs. Because he no longer dared to close his eyes, he had fixed them on the cracks of the window awaiting the first light of dawn. Unbeknownst to him, Ramadin's mother had also gone through a bad night. She did not share her dream, thinking that it was a woman's matter. But she did place her hand on her breasts to ascertain that the echo she had always felt as a young girl was still audible to her failing sense of hearing. She remembered that her echo had failed only once before. It had happened after she had given birth to Ramadin. Fear had forced her to take her newborn to the great-mother at the end of the village near the Cave of the Serpent.

"You must get your milk back and place it on his lips so that he can find his place among the living," she had been told as she had prepared to leave. But a second warning froze her at the door step. "From now on you must face the forces of forgetfulness that have been snatching our young ones from the village." The poor woman had spent the rest of her life trying to prevent her son from following in the footsteps of the others. But on the day of the procession to the train station to gather the boxes with the remains of the soldiers, the mother had taken the liberty of turning her mind away from her mission. At that very moment, her brief concern for the soldiers in blue uniforms set in motion the events that were to lead to the loss of her own son. What awaited her was a cycle of time woven in guilt that would gnaw at her until the last moment of her life.

Ramadin, soaked in sweat, reached the café in the square of the main fountain. He looked for an empty seat outside. "He looked like a frightened stray dog trying to avoid being chased away," the others would remember years later. The few almond trees in the square that had weathered the cold winter were immersed in loneliness. The swallows had failed to return from the African shores, but Ramadin paid no attention to the absence of the birds. The blue stones carpeting the square seemed to be making knots with the sun rays bouncing back and forth in the mirrors of the water gushing out of the mouths of the gargoyles of the old fountain. The weather-beaten door of the Church of the Dead had been closed as if forever. The cats that generally stretched to the intense heat of the day on the steps of the church were not to be seen.

Seated alone outside the café, Ramadin had the feeling that something strange was lurking in the square. His right hand quivered uncontrollably. On the right side of the church, he saw Vlasë returning along the winding brook from his vegetable garden. Vlasë was the first to rise in the village. While everyone else in Sheshi was still between the night and the rise of the sun from the lowest of the seven mountains, Vlasë had already tended to the tender shoots of his plants.

From a distance, Vlasë and Ramadin exchanged an uncertain greeting with a slow movement of their right hands. Ramadin was convinced during that exchange that he detected a helpless feeling of sadness in Vlasë's hazy gray eyes. They looked at each other one last time as Vlasë turned to face the narrow street of his home. A sudden pain in Ramadin's abdomen had begun to blur his vision. Around him, darkness was descending. The familiar corners of the square had vanished. Blood gushed from his neck, creating a pool in front of his chair. He fell over head first, drawing his last breath in his own blood, his wide-open eyes laden with fear.

"I did not see from where the shot had been fired," Rina told the authorities. "I was sitting mending my husband's woolen socks behind the balcony with the door ajar when I caught sight of Ramadin falling into the pool of blood. I did see Vlasë near the Church of the Dead raising his hand to greet Ramadin. The shot must have been fired when I leaned over to pick up the needle that had fallen. I tell you, I did not see anyone else in the square. I tried to open the door to the balcony but my arms had melted. I did see Ramadin trying to lift himself up, but his body fell back again like a cat curling next to the fireplace."

On Vlasë's street, the few people who had not gone to the train station swore, when asked, to have seen Vlasë wipe the tears from his eyes with the right sleeve of his shirt. The exact time at which the neighbors saw Vlasë could not be verified since, had they possessed a clock, they would have been unable to read it. "It was just before the sun stretched its wings on top of the red clay hill. We had just finished hanging the tomatoes on the front wall of our homes," they had said.

Vlasë lived by himself in the last house of the ravine. It was a cave dwelling of volcanic stones that he had collected and chiseled with the greatest care. It was the place his great-grandfather had initially carved from the mountain and for which his own father had built the first fireplace. Vlasë still felt their presence and still nourished their memories. How long ago that was, Vlasë could not tell. But he had seen many sunrises and many moons appear over his house. He suspected that the house must have been carved before the village was called Sheshi and much before he had decided never to speak again.

Late that evening, the authorities did descend to the bottom of the village with the hope of getting some answers to their questions concerning Ramadin's death. By the time they got there, the setting sun had been replaced by a full moon. The sudden appearance of the moonlight from behind the dark blue clouds made their descent much easier. To the Mayor it was impossible to believe that Vlasë could have been responsible, but he had to follow every lead to get to the bottom of the killing. What disturbed him the most was the timing. "How could they have killed Ramadin on the day they were collecting the boxes with the remains of the soldiers amidst the silence of the early afternoon?" the Mayor mumbled to himself even as he approached Vlasë's home.

The Mayor found Vlasë seated on the stone stool in front of his house. For the Mayor and the lawman, Vlasë had but one answer, which he gave with a stutter, due to his long-standing habit of silence. "I saw death in his eyes the minute I saw him in front of the café. Later on, I smelled the dead body left to decay, and I knew that Ramadin had gone to the other side of the brook where the wheat fields never cease to dance with the wind. I had waved at him with my right hand, for with the other I was carrying the few red tomatoes I had gathered from the vegetable garden. I did that, feeling very sad inside of me, just the way I felt when I had to bury the ashes of my own son, killed in the deep snows of the country that has neither beginning nor end. At least, that is how Prefti Vlasë explained it to me after the service at the Church of the Dead." The Mayor saw no reason to ask Vlasë any more questions.

Ramadin's body was wrapped in a white sheet and fresh violets were sprinkled over it. Placed on top of the kitchen table, it took three days for everyone to view. Emira did not shed one tear. She pulled the rocking chair that had been in the family for so long up next to the window that overlooked the street. Those who passed by saw her face change from that of an angel to that of an old fairy with white, disheveled hair. The memory of Ramadin and Emira remained forever fixed in Darius's mind. He stated that their presence would be felt across the ocean for as long as the fountain would bring water from the depths of the seven mountains. And, indeed, the last letter we received from the village did mention that plans had been approved to restore every fountain to life.

The only newspaper stand at the corner of Jackson Avenue and One Hundred and Forty-Ninth Street was surrounded by curious onlookers. The Indian attendant from Madras watched them carefully as they glanced at the headlines. "Mass killings in a rice field." Photographs showed naked children overcome by fear. An elderly woman, her hands reaching to the sky, appeared to me unmoved by the scene on the roadside, while, in the distance, a long line of people followed one another in procession. This was the photograph which was to divide the neighborhood. A few from the high offices gloated over the conflict. The rest anxiously waited for a prompt resolution to a war about which they knew very little. The pain of the terrorized naked children was being swallowed quickly by the stream of automobiles moving along the main avenue. Tempers flared from the college campus to the streets, pitting the youth, carrying peace signs, against the old, puffed up with fake arrogance.

That same afternoon the mailman personally delivered a letter to Darius. Because it was truly addressed to him, the heavy envelope caught everyone's attention, but it revealed nothing of the contents which were to change the family for years to come. Darius was summoned to report to the main army center of the city the very next day. The envelope even held a copper subway token. I read the letter over and over again, as if trying to find a word that could shed some doubt upon its main demand. The expression of sorrow in our sister's face spoke of terrible things to come. Saying nothing, she rose to find the old rope-bound suitcase which Father had brought from the village. Sister spent the remaining hours of the night washing and ironing Darius' few belongings. She also tucked in a picture of each family member, which she had sewn into a cloth pocket sprinkled with a few pellets of moth balls. She cautioned Darius to keep them in a safe place. "We will be there for you during the long, rainy days that bring out the loneliness in a person."

"How far away is this place where he is being sent with the rest of the young men we have been seeing on the television?" she asked me.

"It is in the direction from where the sun rises in the early hours of the morning," I replied. I could tell by her looks that she was not reassured by the answer, but she was convinced that the pictures she had sewn into his left pocket would help him find his way back home.

The next morning, pushing against a cold wind, we accompanied Darius to the train station where Jackson Avenue met the tall buildings of the projects. The station was deserted. The rush hour had passed, and the neighborhood had already fallen into its daily slumber. "We will be waiting for your return," Sister told Darius as the train approached from the north side of the city.

"I'll be back after I see what the world looks like on the other side of the neighborhood," he said in fear and wonder. Those were the last words we were to hear from him for months. Sister waited anxiously for the first letter to arrive. The humid summer days seemed to linger longer than usual.

Autumn had not yet made its presence known upon the leaves of St. Mary's Park when a rain storm hit and we awoke to a cold morning. The rain quickly turned into ice crashing against the window panes. The steps of the tenement home had been emptied for the season. The women had retired to places behind the window glass, where they continued waiting for their loved ones to return. An air of seclusion nestled over the rooftops and dark clouds cloaked every building on Jackson Avenue. This time, the silence of long ago had made its way into the house, determined to lodge there forever. Through the night, it turned into a visible shadow feeding on the moonlight.

Months later, with a distant smile upon her face, Sister announced the imminent arrival of a letter. "Buy some potting soil," she directed me. "The herbs on the window sill need to be replenished."

A few days later, a letter did arrive. The postman confessed to the difficulty he had had in finding the street written in large letters on the envelope. "I had to find an opening through the iron fence to deliver the letter," he complained as he cleared the dust from his light blue uniform. "I asked the few people wandering in the street where number 506 was, but no one remembered."

In fact, our tenement was the only one still standing between One Hundred Forty-ninth Street and Jackson Avenue. The others had disappeared under piles of bricks and decayed wood. I saw the changes coming as fast as the northern clouds that made their appearance at the end of summer. I tried to give an account to Sister, who had completely stopped venturing out since Darius' departure for the distant war. Time had taken hold of everyone in the neighborhood and was determined to erase as many old memories as possible in order to make room for the new waves of people who had settled on the east side of St. Mary's Park. "I don't need to go out to see what is going on," she answered as I attempted to keep her informed of the changes. "I prefer to breathe the same air we breathed together when we came here from Sheshi."

Bent upon keeping alive every single detail of our journey from the village to the city, Sister had stubbornly refused to acknowledge the havoc of time right outside the window of her room. To preserve the echoes and the odor of her herbs, she sealed every opening, converting the apartment into an enclosed cage. The thick walls, laden with memories which nourished one another, excluded the events of the street. The postman noted an odd sensation; as he climbed them, the piles of bricks had seemed to multiply the closer he came to the entrance of the tenement. "I only stopped to catch my breath and to see what was ahead of me, while the sky got darker and darker behind me," he said as he searched for the letter inside his leather sack.

Although it was the last building standing, the owner to whom I paid the rent at the end of the month refused to give the place up to the city. "You'll be staying there for as long as I live," he would tell me, his blue eyes hiding behind a gray veil. Not long after, his health rapidly failing and his eyes ever more clouded, he closed down his butcher shop on the main avenue and admitted that the city was closer to succeeding in its scheme. The disease afflicting him had turned the owner into a small child with an innocent smile that inevitably made others respond to him in kind. The last time I saw him, I could only recognize his voice. His eyes were half-closed and colorless. He had been placed in a wooden cradle in front of the window.

"You'll be told when you have to vacate the apartment," the elder son told me in a tone that left no space for protest. I left the butcher shop as the cradle began to shake violently. I could see the eyes of the small creature bulging from their sockets and opening long crevices in the large front window. Outside, the sky had filled with dark clouds running on top of each other and sending down sheets of rain.

"We have to find another place to live," I told Sister.

"I already know we have to move. I was told in a dream as I held an abandoned child. He was hungry, but I had no milk to give him in my breasts and there were no mountains nearby to offer us wood for the winter." Sister was aging as fast as the seasons that came and went without leaving anything to grasp.

That night, the storm having taken out the electricity, I read her the letter by candlelight. It had been written weeks ago. In it, Darius spoke of the rigorous training over beaches, forests and deserts. "I am forbidden to ask anyone where we are to be sent, but I had heard two bunk-mates in the lower tier say that we're to be shipped to a place where the rainy season never ends and where villages are washed away," he wrote at the bottom of the page.

Months later, the place many called "Hell" was on the

front page of every newspaper. The French had become stuck in the quicksand and were waiting to be rescued. The newcomers had entered a green labyrinth from which there was no exit. It had become a terrible war. Infinite plastic bags holding the dead began to arrive during the silence of the night. From every point of the city, one could smell the presence of death. The sky was weaving clouds and a windless atmosphere intensified the foul air, keeping everyone at home. Windows were kept shut and all the openings sealed to keep the smell out. Angry crowds gathered daily in front of the government building, demanding the burial of the plastic bags stacked on the city's piers. The demonstrators were met by an army of law enforcers who left dozens of the protestors bleeding on the ground. The law officers were joined by hundreds of construction workers, each with a flag and a steel pipe; together, they attacked the bearded students who questioned the country's involvement in an unjust war. The indiscriminate killing of the war and the attacks on the demonstrators made their way into every home through the television screen.

Marooned in our apartment, Sister grew concerned that Darius would not be able to find his way home because of the changes to the neighborhood. The place had become unrecognizable. The elevated train at the end of Jackson Avenue stood much taller than ever. Rebuilding would have to wait until the war came to an end. But the war dragged on and the city itself grew indifferent to the many deaths announced daily in the newspapers and on the television. It wasn't long before the city lost count of all its dead soldiers coming back in plastic bags. The cemetery on the northern edge of the city turned into a year-long field of flowers.

Months went by with no further letters from Darius. At home, Sister looked more and more like Mother. It seemed as if the past had found its way into the realities of the present. Events moved in a circle. They came and went with the same urgency of yesteryears.

On a cloudless morning of an indeterminate season, I found myself sitting next to the fireplace in our home in Sheshi. I had just turned the olive log to create a flame. The home smelled of freshly-picked olives, much as the whole village did in the last days of November. From the balcony, the sky was filled with suspended white flakes glittering over the threads of the moonlight peeking furtively from the dark clouds. The crumbling wall in front of the house still faced the old clock on the tower of the municipal building. The plants growing on the retaining wall had not lost their indefinable scent. It seemed as if time had stood still forever.

Inside the house, the few pieces of furniture were dustless. The rocking chair next to the balcony had retained all its solitude. On the small table next to it, the crochet needles eagerly waited to restart knitting. I was waiting for father's whistle from beneath the balcony; this was the signal to prepare the evening meal. The first to arrive was his yellow finch, who flew back into the cage which hung on the wall of the balcony. The days were short or long, depending on the season, and the activities in each home in Sheshi were synchronized to the status of the growth of the plants in the fields. Each person knew exactly what was to be done. The inscrutable faces of the women of old had grown in silence and had come to occupy the invisible places. Their world was as impenetrable as the thick walls that supported the house.

There were six of us at that time in our home in Sheshi. The youngest of the family, Darius, was to be baptized. The wooden cradle had been placed in the middle of the room in readiness, and the women seated around the perimeter of the house complained of the priest's tardiness. I lingered with the rest of the children on the front steps where the sun had already warmed the stones.

The first to arrive was Father. He kept the barber shop open until midday. At times, it took only a few customers to feed the family. While he waited for them, Father paced back and forth in the main square with his eyes fixed on the road that led to the train station. Watching him from the steps of the Church of the Dead, I often felt as much pain and anxiety as he did. The loneliness that took over the square at midday was broken only by the shrieks of the black swallows flying straight into the pool of water at the base of the fountain. The seven mountains grew taller as the sun moved above them marking the line of descent.

The baptism ended with the pouring of the Holy Water over the head of the recent addition to the family. The women could not stop commenting on Prefti Vlasë's drunkenness. With the approaching darkness, the festivities quickly came to an end. One by one, the guests returned home to prepare for work in the fields the next morning.

From below the ravines, the winds were gathering strength deep within the crevices. The time had come for the people of the village to plug their ears with cotton balls to protect themselves from the piercing howls of the wind. That year, the winds lasted longer than usual. Soon after, dark clouds arrived from where the sun rises, cooling the air during the day and freezing it at night. The olive trees began to lose their leaves and, unprotected, the green olives dropped one by one. The elderly in Sheshi were at a loss to explain what was happening, for no one could remember anything like it in the past. Some attempted to chant the almost-forgotten songs to induce dreams that could dig deep into their memories. It was all in vain. An army of black swallows darkened the sky for weeks, and the olive trees were stripped bare. Whole families began to take the road that led to the train station. Soon after, without hesitation, Father closed the barber shop. He padlocked the door with the lock that had belonged to his great-grandfather. Later, Sister would never fail to polish a replica of the lock with white vinegar and to replace it safely inside the chestnut box on Jackson Avenue.

The only place that remained open in Sheshi was the café in the main square. The place became an open confessional. There people disclosed their plans for leaving the village and received advice from those who had seen the outside world. The light in the café shone until early dawn when the door was locked and the square was left to the stray dogs and wandering cats. "If we are to survive the coming winter, I must reach my sister across the ocean." Father uttered those words as we all sat around the fireplace. The last log was burning slowly, giving out just enough heat to make us almost feel its warmth. Early the next morning, we all watched Father fill a small sack with dried figs, a bottle of olive oil and a handful of chestnuts that Mother kept fresh inside a barrel filled with soil. Father traveled on foot for two days to reach the public notary in the town with the hunting castle. "Tell my sister," he directed, "that I must leave the village with my two oldest children so that the rest can go on living. Say also that it is not my intention to leave our parents all alone in the cemetery. As you well know, I have kept vigil over them for years and no one in Sheshi can reprimand me."

"Master Dunati, you are doing what many of us will have to do one day and what many others have done before us," replied the public notary.

Thereupon, an uneasiness settled over our home as

Father waited for the letter to come from across the ocean. Winter had arrived early and seemed in no hurry to leave. In the village the people suffered in silence, putting all their hopes on better times to come. Some prayed for an early spring and an abundant wheat harvest that would keep the young men busy at least until the end of June. But the young were like birds in a nest waiting for their wings to grow stronger and longer. It was the loss of the young ones that filled the elders with a pain they never dared to mention.

The cold nights gave way to a dense fog that enveloped each home and detached the villagers from one another. Mother had put away the remaining candles for future days. The only source of light was the faint flame in the fireplace. Darkness, a constant presence in our home, erected even thicker walls than the fog outside. Mother and Father exchanged very few words. The pile of wood was almost gone. The heavy snows in the mountains had prevented a distant uncle named Udhë from replenishing the logs.

Uncle Udhë lived in a village on the other side of the seven mountains. He had come back from across the ocean with a small fortune and had bought a parcel of land at the edge of town. The war quickly gnawed at his estate. The government took over his precious woods, leaving him nothing but dead trees to harvest. Uncle Udhë felt cheated twice by the people in power and spent the rest of his youthful years trying to find his way back to the lands across the ocean. "It is only a matter of time before I leave again," he told the few people who sat with him on the steps of the old stone church, waiting for the sun to hide behind the chain of mountains. In the end, he sat alone as the years went by, dreaming of the land where work abounded and the table was always covered with food and one could wipe the sweat from his brow with satisfaction. "Here, there is no future. You become a slave as soon as you open your eyes, and when you die, there may not even be anyone to close them for you."

The annual trip he took across the mountains to sell the wood in Sheshi fetched him a gallon of olive oil and a sack of chestnuts. The color of the sky and the sweetness of the air told him when to take the trip back to his village. He knew which path to take and which slopes to avoid better than any one else. The years he had spent in the land across the ocean had given him the confidence that was lacking in the others. "He has the strength of our ancient gods," murmured those who saw him climbing towards the seven mountains.

Time began to play tricks on Udhë. Only a few images of the land across the ocean remained alive. He saw them clearly when he closed his eyes in the fulness of the night. "I don't even share those memories with your sister," Udhë told Father as they cracked a few roasted chestnuts and savored a glass of wine next to the fireplace. "Your sister is convinced that the body and mind have to work together, for if they separate, they will tear apart entirely. I think she is right, although I feel the need to share those memories with someone and I know that you don't mind listening to me. Besides, they could be of use to you when you leave the village to join your other sister."

Udhë's comments filled Father with fear. He rarely entered the conversation and allowed Udhë to speak freely and unopposed until the first rays of sunlight announced his departure. The one who absorbed every sound and color of the conversation was Udhë's son, Gaetani, who always accompanied his father on those long trips across the seven mountains. A few years later, Gaetani left the village to search for work beyond the white mountains where the people were as orderly as the big clocks in the belfries that guarded their valleys. On that day, father and son said good-bye to us with the certitude that great changes were about to come to both families. "If the winters do not stop getting longer, I may not be able to cross the mountains next year," Udhë said as his mule started the ascent towards the first hill.

Not long after the departure of Gaetani, Uncle Udhë left one morning to gather wood on the south side of the forest below his village. He never returned, although his mule, laden with chopped wood, did make his way back. Out of necessity, a relative sold the mule in the village market more than once, for whoever bought it would lose it the very next day. Daily the mule descended into the forest to wait for Uncle Udhë at the first signs of darkness. The search for the owner went on for months. The family no longer attempted to sell the mule. They became convinced that the faithful beast rode with Udhë during the silence of the night to provide wood for all the homes in the villages around the seven mountains.

Filumena was the oldest living member of the Boletini family. Her grandfather had carried her on his shoulders as they escaped the burning wheat fields on the other side of the sea where the sun still bleeds memories. I remember Father telling us that his own father had made the difficult decision of sending his daughter across the ocean at a tender age to find work with the help of her great-uncle. "The burden of that decision weighed so heavily on him that he never mentioned her name again as we sat all together around the fireplace."

Chapter Nine

Aunt Filumena left Sheshi with five lire sewn inside her dress. It was all the savings that the relatives had been able to gather. "Try not to spend any of it," her father had admonished as they were about to reach the city under the volcano. "You are going to need it as you disembark from the tall ship." She was half asleep and not yet fully a woman. She had just begun to see things with her own eyes. The starry sky touching the few burning lights in the city brought a distant smile to her face. Aunt Filumena was traveling with fifteen other young girls, led by her father's best friend. He promised to take care of her until she could reach her great-uncle. In return, Grandfather had promised to take care of the latter's land and to have it ready for planting when he returned. They had come to trust one another since they had found each other by chance hiding in the same ravine after the uprising in the village on the other side of the Adriatic Sea. From that moment on, they watched after each other's family as if it were one. They also made it a point to keep alive the memories of their burned village in the eyes and hearts of their siblings.

With Aunt Filumena's departure, the house filled with unmentioned sadness. A deep sense of guilt had penetrated every crevice in the four walls. Grandfather did not know whom to blame for having to send his eldest daughter across the ocean to help out her younger sisters and brother. Grandmother had only one answer: it was best not to desire things that are out of reach. She rarely spoke, but she walked as if she had the strength to defy even fate.

"I cried until there were no more tears to shed," Aunt Filumena confessed to me as she struggled to grasp her last breath of air. "It was the ocean with waves as high as the very mountains I used to watch in Sheshi as I gathered water for the evening meal from the fountain that made me realize that I was being sacrificed by the family. The long voyage left me with a bitter taste that only grew worse with the years. Now, as I find myself more alone than ever, that bitter taste even takes my sleep away."

She had spoken to me with a need to share her intimate secrets, and a clear sign of relief made its way from her pale blue eyes as she became certain that her memories would not drown in the sea of forgetfulness. She told me where to find her pile of letters. She had spent each minute of her free time trying to find a compelling reason for her father's decision to send her across the ocean. Each letter wove together every event of her life.

"I never saw any of the money inside the green envelope they gave me at the end of the month. My great-uncle's only comment was that he would mail the money to my father. I saw very little of the family as I spent more and more hours at the textile mill. The sweatshop was like a never-ending tunnel. At the crack of dawn, each one of us took her place at a machine and, but for the briefest of breaks, did not rise again until the long siren at sunset. We exchanged very few words, and then only to ask for news from Sheshi. I saw mothers and daughters wither away there until the day they were replaced with other women. At times I wondered if life for a woman in the village, toiling in the fields under the hot sun, was any worse than the one I found in the sweatshop. The rats were something else. They never failed to gather around us during our fifteen-minute break. They were just as hungry as we were, but they shared the few crumbs that fell and disappeared as soon as we returned to our places.

"On hot days, I missed the cool breeze that descended to our home in Sheshi from the chestnut grove above the train station where I had played with my rag doll away from my parents. I got to know each of the trees and had secretly given them names. Those trees never failed to bring the biggest chestnuts in all the lands around the village. In fact, the grove became a hiding place for most of the young girls of Sheshi. The trees spoke a language that only we understood as we embraced them, feeling a vibration that seemed to seep from the exposed roots that girded each tree. That is how we grew up with each passing season and it was with a sense of loss of something we could neither explain nor prevent. What it might have been just vanished when the first cold wind descended from the mountains. In early winter, the mountains seemed to want to touch the sky before slumbering away. The blue sky was tainted with streaks of gray. I never saw that sky outside the sweatshop. Most of the time, the sky was covered with the dark fumes that belched from the tall chimneys at each end of the brick building. Even when we sat together for our fifteen-minute break, we could not see it.

"Once a month, my great-uncle wrote a letter to Mother and Father as if in my own words. 'I am working hard and I enjoy what I am doing. At the house, they are all kind to me. I hope the money I am sending you is of help. It is all that I can earn for now. Give a kiss to my sisters and brother. You are always in my thoughts. I hope one day to be together with you all.'

"Nights were frightening to me. I felt as lonely as my grandmother's tomb in the cemetery, where I could not place a candle on All Souls' Day. We rarely ventured out of my great-uncle's house. He did not want his children to be exposed to the insults of the neighbors. They did not look kindly at us and always whispered something that sounded like the growling of a dog. I did not at first understand what they were saying, but, with the passing of time, the strange sounds became familiar and I was able to distinguish one house from another.

"The big war came and the streets filled with much more anger. The eyes of some of the neighbors bulged like the eyes of an owl. In the sweatshop, we worked longer hours than usual. The workers' faces changed every so often. Some would leave and would never be seen again. Others came and took their places without ever raising their eyes. We switched to making soldiers' uniforms. 'The government wants you to work more for less. We have to give back what they gave us,' the owner reminded us every morning as we saluted the flag and pledged allegiance to it.

"I learned of the war at my great-uncle's house. It had been going on for months. I did not know why they were fighting, nor who was involved in it until one evening while my relatives listened to the radio with every window shut. 'Make certain the children stay at home after school. It will be dangerous from now on to leave them unwatched in the street. This war against our people is going to create troubles for us,' my great-uncle said to his wife.

"It took only a few weeks for the town authorities to appear at my great-uncle's house. The four men, all dressed in black, had parked their automobile in front and waited until they saw him get off the trolley at the main street and walk straight to the house. My great-aunt, who had been sewing at the window, had noticed their presence hours before. She was waiting to see her husband walking down the street as she did day after day. But that late afternoon, he failed to look at the upstairs window as he always did the minute he stepped off the trolley. For all the years he had spent in the new land, he still could not understand the language well enough to give an immediate answer to the men. One of them walked straight towards him, revealing a badge.

"That evening, my great-uncle and they spoke in the dining room for more than one hour, but to us it seemed as long as the nights during the hot summer months. When the four men left, he gathered everyone together and told us the details of the conversation. 'They wanted to know if I belonged to the party of the Black Shirts and if I spoke in our language to you. At least, I think that is what one of them was asking. It was difficult to tell because he spoke our language poorly. I told him that at home we spoke an ancient language given to us by the gods through the eagles that still roam on those lands and not the language he used in speaking with me.'

"Only much later did I learn that it was forbidden to speak the language of the enemy. At home, after that evening, we began to point at things instead of uttering their names. Life there went on like that for more than two winters. In the early spring of the third year, news came from all directions and especially from the neighbors, who abruptly changed their hostile attitude toward us. My great-uncle became more confused than ever. We still did not know what the war had been all about and, particularly, what we had had to do with it.

"Letters from Sheshi had not reached me for the longest time, but when they did arrive finally, each was more desperate than the previous one. There was famine in all the villages around the seven mountains, and the wheat fields were filled with the bodies of thousands of soldiers. 'We have been burying whatever limbs we could find so that the pain of the relatives would be less. The air at times smells like the underground of the church in the cemetery where they still keep the bones of our dead. The animals in Sheshi have been frightened for so long that they can no longer be tamed. This year it was impossible to plant the wheat because the land is pocked with craters made by the bombs that never stopped falling from November until the end of December.'

"Those who had spoken in favor of the war left, fearing for their lives. Brother had turned against brother and, in some cases, there was even shooting between fathers and sons. 'The nights have turned into acts of revenge. The early hours of the morning are used to clear the streets of the dead. The youngest of your sisters, so frightened by the violence, has not spoken a word since they started to collect the dead bodies of the soldiers along the brook below the ravine of Old Sheshi. The boys have stopped growing, even though the years are clearly visible on their foreheads. Prefti Vlasë has told us that the world moves backwards when the Devil rules. He predicted that, sooner than we could imagine, we would be moving back to the caves at the edge of the village with all our animals. He has warned us of the peril of losing our souls if we fall for the sweet words of the new order that preaches equality for everyone and the abolition of private property. Your mother is no longer with us. She decided to leave the burden of raising and caring for your sisters and brother to me. I did not know what was inside your mother's mind, although some nights I heard her sobbing. I guess the war and the pain of seeing the hunger in the eyes of those she had given life was too much for her to handle. I found her hanging from the old fig tree above the train station.

"'I tried to sell that piece of land even though I had saved it to put together the dowry for two of your sisters, but no one would buy it. People still claim to hear her crying into the night as they return home from their own fields. They say that the cry is like a wound that does not close but rather bleeds more and more as one becomes aware of it. I have been taking her water and bread every day as I was told to do by the elders near the cave of the sacred serpent until thirty-three days shall have come and gone. After that, I have been assured, her soul will find rest among our dead in that corner of the cemetery that looks toward the sunset.

"'The oldest of your sisters is carrying a big burden now, but, if God wills it, she will soon have a family of her own. A young man, who has been in the land across the ocean and by chance was in the same town where your great-uncle has his home, found the image of the blue river he had been looking for right in your sister's eyes. He is not from our own village; he came to ours after he had been told that her eyes carried the color of the fabled river. Every day she looks more and more like your mother. Those who have forgotten the coming and going of the seasons still call her by your mother's name. She made a pact with her husband-to-be that their first child should carry the name of your mother and be cleansed with the waters from the sacred cave.

"'I am happy to say that her future husband has consented to every wish your sister has expressed. We will depend on her as we depend on you to feed the rest of the siblings.'

"I remember saving these letters, along with those written to me by the trembling hand of the postman, in a pine box that smelled of pine resin. After trying fruitlessly to decode the secret messages and failing to distinguish one letter from another, I burned all of them. At first, I felt sorry for the young mail deliverer because of the sadness I saw in his eyes and because of his inability to say anything when he handed me the letters. He never failed to walk up the steps of the house whether there was mail or not; when he reached the top stair, he would pretend to search inside his leather pouch for anything that had our name. Then he would leave with a single wave of his hand, only to reappear the next day at exactly the same time. Everyone at the house got so used to seeing him at the precise hour of the day that there was no need to look at the only clock we had, which hung on the kitchen wall where the window stood overlooking a tall sycamore tree in the back yard.

"I began to feel a strange uneasiness that kept me awake during the night. I also began to hide behind the window on the second floor waiting for the postman to turn the corner at the street above ours. It was then that I also started to sense an urge similar to the one a mother has when she first places the tender mouth of her baby next to her nipple. A muddled desire had begun to surge from the hollow recesses of darkness. It was much later that I learned that it was part of growing up, a preparation for severing one bond and establishing another.

"There came a time not long after a very cold winter that caused a lot of deaths, especially among the elderly, when I began to see the postman's face everywhere I looked. At first the apparitions frightened me because they revealed the effects of time in that his initial look of sadness had turned to one of complete resignation. This feeling of futility was never to leave him.

"I decided to write a letter to my father explaining what was happening to me. I did not mention anything to my great-uncle. By this time I had learned to write from the others with whom I worked and to receive mail there. I remember the bright clear day when I received the response from Father. 'There is a letter for you at my desk,' the floor supervisor said. 'You can pick it up after work on your way home.'

"The envelope smelled of eucalyptus flowers, similar to those that still grow in the olive groves around Sheshi overlooking the barren hill tops from where we saw the red poppies sail with the spring breeze as we chased white butterflies. Father understood everything I had asked him. 'We are happy to learn that you have become a woman and are ready to start your own family,' he wrote. 'I only ask that you not forget your sisters and, especially, your brother, who, as the last born, is growing very frail without your mother's love. Lately he has become taciturn, and his eyes bear swirling scars when they look at me. I decided to apprentice him to the village barber. If what your great-uncle has told me is true, he will one day make a decent living in the big city across the ocean. I am convinced that he has inherited the sickness of all the young men who want to leave Sheshi, although he has not mentioned a word of it to me. Perhaps one day when you have settled down with your own family in your own home you will be able to save the money to sponsor him. But my real concern is the youngest of your sisters. She has grown into a full woman faster than I expected her to. She has received the best features from your mother's family and mine to the point that her beauty has become a worry to me. For awhile, during the height of summer, she had all the young men of the village daydreaming. They would walk back and forth below our balcony trying to catch a glimpse of her face. A week ago, a circus came to Sheshi and your sister did not miss one performance. She was taken by the skill and feats of a young trapeze artist who did somersaults on top of a wire landing, at times, on just one foot. Your sister followed him to the next town across the barren hills. It took me three days to find her and bring her back home. We returned to Sheshi at night so as not to let anyone know where she had been. Any knowledge of her escapade, as you know, would have ruined her reputation as well as that of her sisters, not to mention the ridicule that your younger brother would have to carry with him for the rest of his life. For this reason, I decided to send her to live with your other sister in her stone house in the middle of the wheat field. Your mother's death left me a terrible burden. Sometimes, as I look down into the square, I wish you were here to be like a mother to your sisters. Your brother is still too young to be burdened with the responsibilities that he has. Now you know why I sent you to your great-uncle's house across the ocean to help me put together a dowry for each of them. I never intended to separate you from us, but I could not see a way out of the misery that was engulfing us and threatening our very existence. One day you will understand how the preservation of one thing requires the sacrifice of many other things.' He closed the letter with his usual reminder that I not fail to write at the end of each month.

"The postman and I decided to ask my great-uncle for permission to marry on Easter Sunday in front of the Church of the Black Madonna. 'Come visit us next Sunday and we will have coffee together,' my great-uncle said to Imiri, pretending not to notice his trembling hand. The following Sunday Imiri showed up with a box of pastries he had bought in his neighborhood where at times he went to sit all alone hoping to recall among all the faces who passed by those of his own parents. But Imiri never learned what his parents looked like. They had died when he was at the threshold of acquiring the memory that was to weave his own life. He grew up in the sacristy of the neighborhood church. That morning he woke up at the crack of dawn, gathered all the strength he could harness and walked unperturbed toward my great-uncle's house. The tone of his voice and his measured words left no doubt in my great-uncle's mind what he had come to demand. 'I have come to claim the hand of your niece.'

"Even had he wanted to prevaricate, my great-uncle had not time. He faced a young man determined to tear down any obstacle in front of him. 'My answer is yes, but I must consult with her father. I shall have my definitive answer by the time I have mailed the letter and received an answer. You just pray for good weather and calm seas so that the ship can deliver the message.'

"The wait for the letter seemed an eternity. The sky darkened for days, sending down rivers of water that forced people out of their houses and onto higher elevations. Others were rescued with long ropes from trees and rooftops as the sky continued to discharge lightning. Soon after, floating homes began their voyage towards the ocean. Grounded Canadian geese twirled their necks and remained motionless. These heavy rains were followed by weeks of intense heat and unbearable humidity. The ground soon cracked, opening deep crevices which threatened to swallow the few remaining houses over the flat lands.

"'If this scorching heat continues, we will have to move closer to the mountains,' asserted my great-aunt.

"'There is plenty of water underground,' my great-uncle reassured her. 'I will just have to dig deeper to tap into it.'

"He knew how important water was for his wife. Water brought to mind her place of birth with no few tears. Her village mirrored the sea, extracting from it the blues for the window panes of her house. On such a clear morning, she had joined groups of young women chosen by the village dressmaker to sail across the ocean to embroider the wedding gown for the last-born daughter of a wealthy family. She had found herself in the waiting room filled with people dressed in their own costumes and speaking languages she could scarcely understand. It was there that she came to see that the world was much bigger than she had been led to believe. The people my great-aunt was able to observe, moreover, did not resemble those of the stories she had heard from her own grandmother. She felt cheated by a reality she had never conceived of existing. After weeks of sailing on a Greek ship where the sailors spoke a tongue similar to hers and of feeling terribly frightened by the huge waves that washed against her small round window, she reached port.

"There all the women were sequestered by the father of the bride-to-be and asked to stitch together the best wedding gown ever to have been sewn anywhere in the world. The fifty women worked day and night beneath the light of the sun and that of enormous candelabras held by black boys who frightened most of the women. They had never seen people with dark skin, minute curls and ivory teeth. 'Their skin must have darkened by being constantly next to the candles,' was their logic. It took these women four full weeks to weave one of the finest wedding gowns ever made.

"The father of the bride called fifty of the strongest men from his steel plant, gave each a bar of Irish soap to wash the grime from their face and hands, and trained them to carry the train of the gown with perfectly coordinated precision. The fifty men, twenty-five to a side and all exactly the same height, formed a perfect entourage for the rest of the world to see. Although the weavers were not invited to the wedding, each received a white flower with a roasted almond affixed."

Aunt Filomena relived moment by moment the last conversation with her mother. "'We will be here waiting for you to come back with some savings so that your father can buy that parcel of land where the sun shines all day long. With that land, we'll have all that we need to face the winters. Besides, you will be going with the other girls from our village. They also are going there for the same reasons.

294

The clerk in the town hall told me that the announcement from the consulate calls for girls who are skillful in weaving, and you are one of the best in the village. Your father was hoping that they would be calling for men, as they did years ago, to work deep in the coal mines, even though the work is dangerous and shortens one's life by half.' Those were the last words I was to hear from my mother.

"Neither I nor any of the other girls could refuse this opportunity. But deep inside I felt a foreboding mingled with an anger that I could not unleash against anyone in the village, for I did not know whom to blame. What I did know, however, was that those who had left the village out of desperation went back years after beaten and changed to the point that they were no longer recognizable. Nor could they regain the road they had left behind.

"But time changes all things even as it itself lasts forever. People are but little pebbles that, unseen by anyone, will one day turn into dust ready to be washed away with the first rains of autumn. Of the thousands of ships that came through the river, the one which had brought us to this land never did return. Daily from my window at home I watched the men load and unload the boats and wondered at the spectacle. Some mothers held their neatly wrapped babies while the more grown up youngsters, their eyes perplexed and curious, held tightly to their mother's long skirts. I waved at them, and they waved back. Then, I would see them no more. It took me a little while to realize that each of those families had a place to go that no one else knew.

"One day, as I stood at the window still waiting for the ship to come back, I saw a young man. I can still see him walking through the street, dressed in a deep blue tie and bearing a dark brown suitcase. It must not have been very heavy, for he walked with a swift, nimble and determined step that left no doubt in the mind of anyone who happened to witness his arrival that early spring morning. The town of Lawrence was up for some changes, and the young man did not hesitate to bring them about the first chance he had.

"During the feast of the patron saint of the poor, he carried the statue of Saint Rock which bore deep scars on one knee and a faithful dog next to the other, licking the wound. This celebration brought people from as far away as one could imagine. Some came by train or bus, but others even had cars to display to the less fortunate. It was an occasion to see and to be seen, to look for a future husband or wife, or simply to meet old acquaintances and reminisce about the old country over a glass of wine. At night, there were music and songs. The elderly sat misty-eyed in front of the raised podium, straining to hear and to keep time with every sound. The young men and women scouted the area barely able to hide their desire to spot someone who stirred their imagination.

"It was during the last of the three nights of festivities that the young man with the face of the Saint being celebrated passed below my window and bade me good evening. Even now, after so many years have gone by, I still can feel the shiver that ran through my body when his voice pierced the glass of the window pane to reach me, leaving behind a clear round hole in the shape of a daisy. That voice was like the sound of a child looking for a familiar face amidst the intense silence of a growing crowd. The determined vibration lodged firmly within my body, giving it new strength and setting my heartbeat to the rhythm of the words spoken. That night I prayed for the celebrations never to end.

"The wind, which had been blowing fiercely all day long, brought to my feet a half-torn page of newspaper with a photograph of a person curled like a cat, almost completely covered in blood. It was the very young man with the saintly face. I learned that same day that he had been beaten to death during a strike to demand better and safer conditions for the textile workers. His killer was never found; I don't even know where he is buried. He had come and gone during the three days of celebration. On a nameless gravestone I placed the picture of the Saint with the Bleeding Knee. I visited the gravesite until I was taken to another city much bigger and busier than Lawrence. It was called Paterson.

"The streets were full of horse-drawn carriages and slow-moving automobiles. The noises silenced the footsteps of the people, and the smoke from the many tall chimneys cast a black veil over the faces of those moving about much like dark clouds on a stormy night.

"We were placed in barracks on the grounds of the tall brick factory, which had as many sewing machines as there were people. These were people with frightened faces, who never looked directly into anyone's eyes. I was placed with those who spoke more or less the way we did in the village. Each one had a story to tell that was never told. It died slowly within each woman in that dim place where humidity turned the air to lead, especially on the hot summer days. The leaves on the few trees I could see from the window quickly turned to brown dust. I held the image of the Virgin of Constantinople and the eyes the color of the sea closer to my chest until I married the postman.

"The postman had secured a job in the textile building to be closer to me. One day in late December he whispered softly into my ear that he had begun to make plans to build me a house bigger than the one in the center of town. 'The front lawn will be full of fruit trees,' he said with a smile that smelled of pure innocence. His determination was like the taste of bread freshly baked. It revived in me the security I had felt at home when we sat altogether waiting for permission from Father to reach for a slice of bread warm from the hearth. His revelation opened my eyes to my childhood dreams and brushed away the darkness of the tunneled sweatshop. For the first time I felt the ground, and I began to notice the many details present in the big city. I breathed more deeply, and I burned with the desire to be the proprietor of one of those houses on the wide avenue and to receive mail with my name on it. The dream was quickly washed away with the coming of the rainy season from the south.

"The supervisor of the plant had begun to send letters of dismissal to many of the workers. 'I am going to have to let you go because I haven't received any more orders from our buyers.' He gave the same line to all the employees. They read the lines the best they could. Things went from bad to worse in just a few months at the textile mill. With the help of the local priests, the women built a shrine at the foot of a spring behind the brick building, but neither the Saint with the Tears in His Eyes nor the flowing waters of the spring could stop the growing lines at every street corner. People waited patiently to get a bowl of soup prepared by those in dark uniforms with an "S" imprinted on the hat.

"The neighborhood was slowly being abandoned. People disappeared overnight to beg for work in the neighboring cities. I could hear the children crying on the surface of the river before the night silenced them. Many of those who had left came back hungrier than before. The others who had been lured into lands of blinding lights were never heard from again.

"I saved all the seeds I could so as to provide for us in the coming winter. Clashes with the police began to occur as days went by and the promises that we would return to work were not kept.

"Starvation had encircled the town. No one dared to speak of it as each family tried to grow as many vegetables as it could in the backyard. The hope of returning to work had begun to wane. The soldiers came and urged the young men to join the army for the preservation of the country and for a better future. The news from Sheshi also spoke of mass killings in many towns. Young men in red shirts sang songs of death. The rivers turned red and the air smelled of burned flesh. Many were forced to drink castor oil in the public squares of the villages by the one in black. Even in our own neighborhood in Paterson the men dressed in black and mocked death. They marched daily singing songs I could not understand.

"Soon the songs turned into screams and the talk of war around the world was the daily conversation among the people gathering at every street corner. It was at this time that your father wrote to me.

"'I have decided to take the two eldest of my children across the seven mountains and cross the ocean. The war has littered the fields with bones. Mothers are feeding roots to their children, for their breasts have gone dry. No one comes into the barber shop anymore.'

"Long periods of drought accompanied the war, and when the rain finally came, the hills of Paterson awoke to a strange odor that filled every house with unknown perfumes. Flowers of all colors had sprouted, climbing trees to garland every window they could find en route to the rooftops. The hills of the town looked like the cover of some of the books I had seen stored in the basement of my great-uncle's house in Clifton. The birds sang and the flowers danced in the winds as the leaves came down from the trees to form a place of rest for the yellow butterflies. 'If these flowers continue to grow the way they have been growing, we'll have to climb over the tree tops to see each other,' the postman, now my husband, would write to me on the white petals that the bluebird, who was building his nest on my window, daily delivered to me.

"The smell of flowers was everywhere. Many forgot their initial sensation of phobia and began to catalogue the variety of flowers that had appeared from the crevices of the dried earth. At times, the thickness of the growth above, and the intricate movements of the stalks growing whichever way they could, left no space unutilized and prevented people from observing the flowers beneath those above. Some, however, were able to record the different hues that changed according to the time of day. The closeness of the place prompted many a person to devise a new language based on the countless colors available. Some even devised specific steps to convert the colors into sound by placing a letter next to each and wrapping them carefully until the people could no longer distinguish the color from the sound.

"Physical changes began to appear in people sooner than expected. In some, the eyes replaced the ears in a matter of weeks, changing completely the shape of the head. The eyes began to function like antennae, opening and closing according to the color that was in front of them. My husband became extremely concerned. There was no need to write any letters because people had simply forgotten how to write from within.

"The telegraph itself was rapidly being replaced by the long arch of the horizon. Each color in it held a code that could only be deciphered by the couples involved. It wasn't long before a long list of color languages were devised with which mother and daughter, father and son, husband and wife could communicate. The one that proved to be the most difficult to standardize was the language of lovers. A special key was needed that only couples could create together.

"For a long time my husband and I flew over places that looked clearer than the dreams that appear just before sunrise. As he grew older, he came to look more and more like the child whom the Madonna holds on the right side of the altar. Sensing that he was slowly withering away, he held onto my skirts, fearful of slipping away from me. We got married with each feeling sorry for the other, in the way that one responds to a plant that is about to shy away from the rays of the sun.

"In two years and a few months we were blessed with two children. They looked as old as we did in only a month's time; days for them became months, and months became years. Sooner than seemed possible, people could not tell us apart. Both of the children fell ill one fall day just before the trees lost their leaves. The two shut themselves in their rooms. It took twelve men to bear them away to a distant hospital, wrapped in the heavy white shrouds with which we bind the dead in our old village. This event utterly silenced their father until the last moment before he expired in that rundown hospital where the rats kept everyone awake through the night. 'We should have stayed up there on top of the horizon, weaving the colors of the dawn with those of the sunset,' was all he was able to say before he lowered his head gently onto the left side of the pillow, taking on precisely the same appearance as that of his son the minute after he was born.'"

That was all Aunt Filumena was able to whisper to me after the last stroke which left her half-paralyzed from her mouth all the way down to her right arm. With the first, the entire left side of her body had shrunk considerably, but not even that could stop her from making soup and preparing coffee for all those who lived in the tenement house. It was the only building still standing, yet she kept basil and parsley growing in flats on most of the window sills. The elderly in the neighborhood considered it to be the last island left, one accessible only to those who still carried the keys of memories. The letters from the old country had stopped coming to Aunt Filumena, although she never ceased waiting for the letter carrier who had stopped crossing the street many years ago.

The morning of our last conversation, my aunt struggled to finish the last words of a letter she was sending to her father. It had taken her left hand months to scribble her pain onto the white page. In the letter she spoke of being tired of waiting for her father to come and get her. "I won't be able to close my eyes," she wrote unsteadily, for the pen moved with her feelings and not with her fingers, "unless you come here. I have been waiting for you to come from the moment I buried the father of my children. Now I would like to come back home and take my place among the people of Sheshi."

Even though the letter was difficult to read, since the page contained scribbling more than anything else, in the spaces between the words was the lucidity of a sky after a heavy storm. I put my aunt's letter away before I arranged a decent burial for her.

In the parlor where the body lay were just a few flowers. The heavy rains that had fallen in the previous hours kept the few people whom she had known in her building for two generations from coming to the wake. Sister and I sat at each end of the first row. I do recall the heaviness of her lifeless body, no longer opposing the magnetic force of matter about to claim it forever. Outside, the dark clouds announced a premature end to the day. The two dim lights on each side of the wall cast the faces of the few people present into shadow.

One of them clasped her fingers nervously. Eyes cast to the floor, she avoided looking at the still powdery body in the plastic inner lining of the coffin. Another, whose heavy breathing could be heard from where I sat, looked fixedly at my sister, whose appearance so markedly differed from everything else that decorated the room.

I looked at my watch. "Just a few minutes before the priest will come in." I had been told by the person in charge that the priest would be arriving at seven.

"He has never been late, although he still walks from his parish here even though it is a good distance away. The rain won't delay him. Once there were two feet of snow on the ground, and still he wasn't a second late." The attendant had scarcely finished this reassurance when the priest, aided by a cane topped with the shape of a dog, walked in. His skin was darker than the long cassock held together by a long file of black buttons; his eyes were two small white circles deeply shadowed by thick eyelashes.

The priest opened his breviary and proceeded with the ceremony without having to turn the page to continue. Clearly, he knew what was written so well that turning the pages was merely a formality in keeping with the requirements of the Church. Yet, his face bore the signs of pain and sadness as he blessed the body, entrusting its soul to God Almighty, "the One who receives us all when the road comes to an end." Taking out his white handkerchief from a side pocket, he blotted sweat from his brow. Then, having been assisted by the attendant in donning his coat and retreating to the front door, the priest turned and bade us goodbye with a lazy gesture of his right arm.

The rain was coming down in sheets by now, hitting the glass windows with fury. "If you wish, you may remain a bit longer," the attendant soothed, although he was obviously in a hurry to close the doors for the night. He knew full well that the heavy rains would not bring any more visitors. One of the elderly ladies murmured something to the other as they made the sign of the cross at the door and closed it gently behind them. The attendant offered them an umbrella he had brought from his office, which they accepted courteously.

My sister and I also left promptly. As the elderly women preceded us to the bus stop a few feet away from the funeral home, I noticed that one of them was limping, one leg being longer than the other. The second, considerably younger and visibly angry, placed the umbrella over the head of her companion. "It seems we are living just to bury the dead," she fumed to me without lifting her eyes from the direction of the bus.

"It is that time in the cycle of things, and it is to be expected," I replied. I knew with certainty that the answer was not going to please her.

The bus was completely empty, but for the driver. It was that hour of the evening in which the streets become naked, revealing the stark callousness of the tenement buildings. The homes differed very little from one another. The suspended fire escapes in front of each apartment dripped showers of corrosion. "The house is too empty without our younger brother," my sister commented, further reflecting the desolation that was all around us. The bus driver seemed anxious to add a few more passengers, delaying a bit longer at each stop and looking all around to see if anyone were running to catch the bus. No one got on, not even at our stop. "Good night,now," he said as he slid the door closed.

The rain continued to come down heavily. "It won't be long before he comes home," I told Sister as we walked toward the house.

The light at the entrance was not lit, and the desolation by now touched the very bones of the neighborhood. "We should never have left the village," she blurted unexpectedly. "Look what has happened to us. One by one they leave, and we no longer have the strength to keep them in our memories. If things keep on happening this way, we won't remember ourselves the way things used to be."

I cloaked myself in silence, for I knew we were losing our battle against forgetfulness. There was no time to waste; we must rush back to the few images deep in the caves of our minds.

The rain had stopped, but it had left a putrid smell in the air. The only lights in the street were those of the corner bar and the passing automobiles sliding over the surface of the wet road. Our tenement house was the only structure still standing among piles of broken bricks and loose mortar. Even the black crows which used to fly over it once in a while had stopped coming months ago. "It will not be long before this last building will also have to come down," Sister observed spiritlessly, avoiding the broken bottles.

The dread of being evicted weighed heavily on her mind. She had accumulated too many little things in that house that kept the past alive. "I am having a tough time keeping all those photographs together. Some of them are turning yellow, and others are developing mold on the surface." She had found a way of keeping those faces fixed inside her own clock. "It is a simple process," she would say. "I learned it from Mother." Sister placed the photographs on the table with a small white candle in front of them. The arrangement created a communicative code understood by her alone. But taking her place among the people in the photographs exacted a heavy price from her; she grew older by the month, her hair now entirely white and her skin barely attached to the bones. Indeed, she started to look more and more like the array of people in those pictures.

Each photograph was encircled in its own time and gave off a pungent odor of unknown herbs. The box where Sister kept the photographs had turned into a multicolored niche. The organisms living in it had carved deep crevices into the nearest walls, until a diffusing scent invaded the entire apartment. Not long after, Sister began to speak with the photographs spread on the table. She seemed totally unconcerned with anything else. It was as if the clocks had been turned back, meeting her unfulfilled desires. At midnight, these folk left the table, one by one, and took their places inside the box, neatly stacked as they had been since the time no one had dared to recall them. In a short time, Sister became an active participant in the appearance and disappearance of the people in the photographs. With each passing day, she became more and more diminutive. She had begun to change into so many forms that I became confused as to which was the real one.

One evening, as I was returning from college much later than usual due to a blackout which had surrounded much of the institution, I found myself engulfed by people coming from all directions. Completely disoriented by the darkness, I had to rely upon mostly unfamiliar sounds, sounds to which I had previously paid no attention. It must have been very late by the time I reached my own neighborhood. An especially bright moon revealed the corroded veins of the bricks on the tenement house. The brittle cement was coming off much faster than I had imagined; worse, still, the fire escape was no longer there. I noticed that the entrance door had been left ajar.

Inside, the walls gasped for air. There was no one to be seen, with the exception of an unusually large black spider in the corner above the window overlooking what had once been the secluded vegetable gardens between the buildings. The intricate spider web reached all the way to the half-open box filled to the brim with photographs. The long thread connecting the two held the secret to the oppressive silence that had taken over all the windows of the apartment house. On the kitchen table I found a note: "Your relative, after a piercing scream, collapsed. Her body can be reclaimed at Montefiore Hospital."

I picked up the picture box and the few books next to it. By then, the silence had almost sealed the exit door with countless layers of slime as dry as old glue. I knew that Sister had taken her place among the people in the photograph.

From the end of the street I turned to glance back at the building; it was no longer there. Rather, the piles of bricks kept growing larger as the bright light of the moon slaked their long thirst. As I waited for the bus to cross the river back to the college, I knew that I was closing a chapter, the remnants of which lay hidden inside the wooden box of photographs.

By now the war had been raging for months, reports of it arriving from foreign news stations. Darius may not have been released yet. "I'll be back on a rainy day," he had said, the day before he had to appear at the military headquarters at the edge of the city where the waters from the wide river became one with the ocean. Upon his return one dreary, rainy day, I saw him searching for the house absent-mindedly as he stood outside the entrance of the corner bar. A faint smile was the only expression on his aged face.

"I have been looking for the house for hours, but I only stumbled upon a pile of bricks," he said with a tone that clearly revealed his confusion.

"The house was condemned a few months ago," I replied.

"The termites had eaten away part of the main beam. The other homes on the block had already fallen on top of each other like a deck of cards. The two sons of the meat-cutter would not spend any money to save the building. Unlike the old man, they did not care for the people living in it.

Although visibly older, Darius' actual age was difficult to guess. The wrinkles on his forehead were beginning to resemble those of Father. In his voice one could hear the resigned tone of one searching for a place to rest after a long day's work. The small green knapsack he carried told the rest of the story. We walked to the bus stop as a steady drizzle soaked our clothes. Chilled and saying very little, we were the only two waiting anxiously for the bus to arrive. It came, sliding noiselessly over the wet road. The red front lights, shining menacingly, barely pierced the thick fog. Only one passenger alighted, but a feeling of vagueness overwhelmed him. Convinced that it was the wrong stop, he scampered back up the steps and asked the bus driver for the name of the location. Satisfied, he descended again and began to walk towards the train station.

Once aboard, Darius and I were the only two passengers. Every now and then, the driver glanced at us quickly in his mirror, not without a certain apprehension. "I will stay for just a few days and then I'll be moving on."

"Where will you go?" I asked, unable to show any concern or disquietude about his plans. His years in the army had erased the childish fear he had brought with him from the village.

"I'll move out west where they say people can plant seeds in every season. I was hoping to see Sister one last time."

"She is much happier with her dreams," was all I managed to say. I did not ask my brother anything else. It was clear that even the years in the army had not erased his childhood memories. His essential core had nourished that child of the past, now ready to take over and to despise the rest of his years. The members of the family had come and gone like the seasons, leaving behind whatever one could gather before they disappeared. This was the last time we rode the bus together.

In my attic room, we went over the photographs, lingering for a long time on each in total silence. Darius chose a few and carefully placed them inside an envelope he drew from the green knapsack. "I will take these with me so that one day I can find my way back to Sheshi." They were the only pictures of our grandparents we had. The old patriarch sat on the wooden chair with Grandmother's hands bashfully placed on his shoulders. Mother had kept the picture frames on the side of the balcony in the one-room house in Sheshi. My grandmother, tall and proud, had inherited all the features of her own mother, adding another layer of bark to the trunk of tree that no wind could tear away.

It was said in the village that our mother spoke with the dead every night after reciting the rosary and that she took no decision without first consulting with them. "With their guidance," my brother now asserted, "I am certain I will find my way back to the village. I have collected all the seeds I could find while the men in my company busied themselves in killing and burning in those lands where the rains never stopped. I will plant the seeds on the hill where our grandmother hanged herself."

I had no reason to doubt his conviction. Now I recalled the words of Master Tuliuci with the clarity I had lacked previously: "Opening the eyes at birth is searching for the road back to the font of memories. Our existence is the labyrinth that each of us must identify and traverse with the help of those who know us better than the others."

Early in the morning we departed, not without a certain fear that neither of us bothered to hide. I saw Darius vanish into the crowd. I could barely make out the arm he raised as he probably looked back before being swallowed by the anonymity of those around him. It was then that I realized that the tie that had held us together was no longer there. In a rush, a deep desire for the warmth of the church steps in the square of Sheshi took complete control of me. The photographs in the wooden box were all that was left of a world I was determined to keep away from forgetfulness.